KINGFISHER EXPLOR

CW00969886

WAR AND WEAPONS

Brian Williams

Designed by David Nash

Illustrators
John Berry · Richard Hook · John Keay · Ron Jobson
Ted Mortelmans · Roger Payne · Charlotte Snook · Bill Stallion

KINGFISHER BOOKS

War and weapons have been part of human history since ancient times. But a warrior from the past would be amazed by the way in which modern wars are fought. During World War II battles were fought on land, at sea and in the air. In 1944, the Allied troops who landed in France were supported by hundreds of ships and thousands of aircraft. The D-Day landing, shown here, was the greatest invasion by sea in the history of war.

3

R. Payne

Every Roman legion carried a standard. The standard on the left is decorated with images of Nero, Roman emperor AD 54–68, and his wife. It was carried into battle by a bearer dressed in a lion skin. It was a great disgrace for a legion to lose its standard.

dagger belt with sword

standard bearer 50s AD

javelin thrower, 100s BC

a Praetorian – one of the emperor's own bodyguards – in battle dress, 100s AD

COH·III·PRI

The Roman Army

The Romans had the best-trained army in the ancient world. They conquered and ruled a huge empire, winning many battles against their enemies.

The army was divided into legions of about 5000 men. Each legion was divided into cohorts of 500 men, and each cohort was made up of centuries (companies of 100 men).

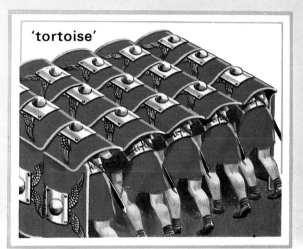

'tortoise'

The officer in charge of a century was called a centurion. All legionary soldiers were Roman citizens. They were tough, disciplined and well-paid.

There were also troops made up of men from the provinces that Rome had conquered. These foreign troops were called auxiliaries, and they were usually used to guard the frontiers. The legions were kept in reserve, ready to march into battle.

The legions could travel long distances quickly along the fine Roman roads. With them went engineers, such as bridge-builders, and the artillery – catapults and other siege weapons. The soldiers set up camps surrounded by a ditch, earthen ramparts and high wooden fences.

phalanx of legionaries, 100s BC

In battle, the legions used clever tactics. The soldiers advanced in a formation called a phalanx – in close ranks and with shields overlapping. The points of their javelins bent easily, so that when they were thrown it was difficult for the enemy to pull them out of their shields. In the confusion, the Romans charged, using their swords and daggers. If they were under fire from spears or arrows, the soldiers formed a square and raised their shields above their heads to make a 'roof'. Protected by this tortoise formation, they advanced further towards the enemy lines.

5

Keay

Siege Warfare

In the Middle Ages kings and nobles built castles to defend their lands. These strong fortresses had thick stone walls and tall towers. Inside was a stronghold or keep. At the entrance was an iron gate called a portcullis. There was often a drawbridge which could be pulled up to keep out the enemy.

An attack on a castle was called a siege. As the enemy drew near, everyone hurried into the castle. Food and water were stored inside, for a siege might last many weeks.

The attackers surrounded the castle to stop supplies getting in. Huge 'siege engines' hurled rocks and spears. Tunnels were dug beneath the walls. And soldiers climbed up ladders and wooden siege towers.

The defenders fought back by pushing away the ladders with poles and setting fire to the towers. They fired arrows and dropped stones and boiling oil on the enemy. Sometimes the defenders ran out of food and water and surrendered. But often the attackers gave up first and marched away. The age of castles lasted until the cannon was invented. Even the strongest castle walls crumbled under cannon fire.

ballista

mangonel

Protected by a wooden hoarding a castle soldier fires on the enemy.

trebuchet

siege tower

scaling ladder

drawbridge

Crossbow and Longbow

In a medieval battle, the most powerful soldiers were knights. They wore fine metal armour and rode on horseback, charging through the enemy with lances, swords, axes and war hammers. The poorer foot soldiers had little or no armour. Some carried spears and pikes. Others had only farm tools.

The best defence against knights was the bow and arrow. English archers used the longbow, made of yew, which could shoot arrows through armour. French archers preferred the crossbow. This powerful weapon fired a short arrow called a bolt, but it took longer to reload.

During the Middle Ages, England and France were often at war. In 1415, King Henry V and his English

army fought a famous battle near the village of Agincourt in France.

The English had only 6000 men, mostly foot soldiers and archers. The French army was much larger. Expecting an easy victory, the proud French knights jostled for a place in the front as they attacked. Crowded together, they made an easy target for the English bowmen, who sheltered behind lines of sharp wooden stakes stuck in the ground.

Many horses were killed as they stumbled over the stakes. On foot the knights could not move easily in their heavy armour. Many were killed or trampled to death by frightened war horses. When the battle was over, fewer than 500 English soldiers were dead or wounded. But more than 5000 Frenchmen had lost their lives. Agincourt had proved that the longbow was the best weapon of the Middle Ages.

CROSSBOW

stirrup

bowstring

bolt

trigger

archer loading crossbow

The first guns were cast in iron or bronze and were very heavy. They fired solid cannon balls.

matchlock of the 1500s

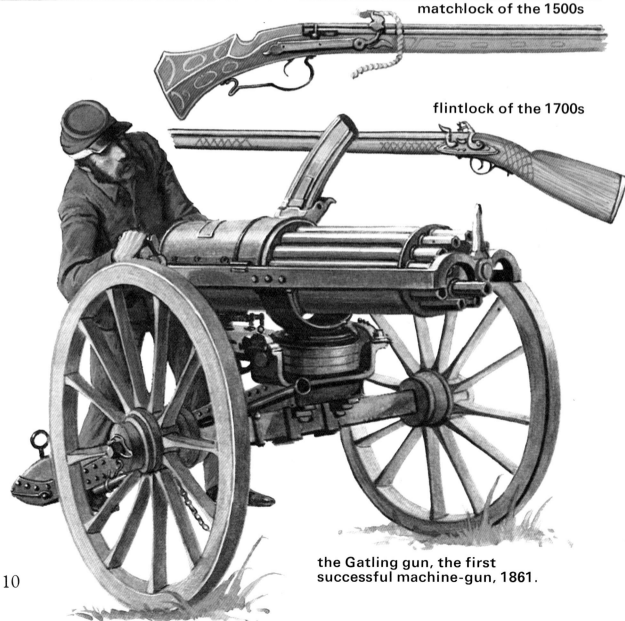

flintlock of the 1700s

the Gatling gun, the first successful machine-gun, 1861.

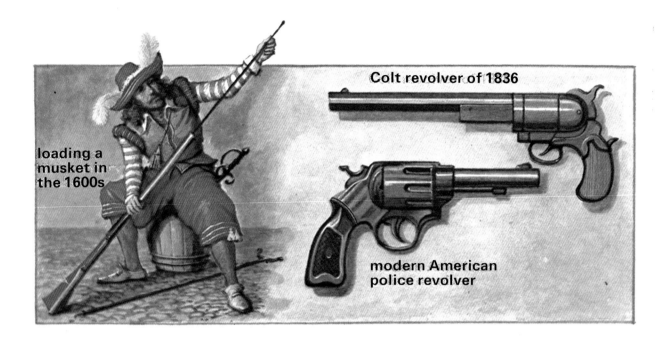

loading a musket in the 1600s

Colt revolver of 1836

modern American police revolver

The Gun

Gunpowder is a mixture of saltpetre, charcoal and sulphur. It was used in the Far East long before the Crusaders brought knowledge of it to Europe. The first guns were large hollow tubes made of metal. They were closed at one end and filled with gunpowder. When a flame was put to a small touch-hole, the powder exploded and shot a metal ball or stone out of the mouth of the gun.

Early cannon were not very accurate. Sometimes they blew up, killing their gunners. Even so, they frightened the enemy, and cannon balls could knock down the thickest castle walls.

The first handguns were rather like small cannon. The matchlock musket was too heavy to hold without a 'rest' to support it and it took a long time to load. When the musketeer squeezed the trigger, a slow-burning match was touched against the powder in a small pan. This 'flash' then set off the main charge.

A better musket, called the flintlock, was invented in the 1700s. Squeezing the trigger made a flint strike a piece of steel so that a spark fell on to the powder. Later, other explosives were used instead of gunpowder. And the firing system of the gun was improved.

In the 1800s, J. R. Gatling invented a ten-barrel revolving rifle which was used in the American Civil War. Other machine-guns soon followed. The most powerful was the Maxim gun of 1884.

Armies needed guns that fired farther and faster. For greater accuracy, barrels were 'rifled' or cut inside with spiral grooves. These spun the bullet, making it fly straighter. And the invention of metal cartridges, each one containing a powder charge and a bullet, made guns easier to load.

The Thin Red Line

Until the 1700s few countries had regular, professional armies. When war broke out, men were called up as soldiers. As soon as peace returned, they went home.

When cannon and muskets replaced bows and arrows, rules of war were drawn up and many regular armies were formed. Rich noblemen formed their own regiments, often dressing their men in handsome uniforms.

Before a battle, the two armies lined up in sight of each other with flags flying and drums beating. Cannon fired, and the infantry (foot-soldiers) marched slowly forwards. They stopped only to fire their muskets at the enemy. As soon as one side's line was broken, the cavalry charged.

Most battles during the Napoleonic Wars were fought in this way. At the battle of Waterloo in 1815, long lines of red-coated British infantry only two ranks deep stood fast against the French cavalry. And the 'thin red line' became famous.

In the 1800s, Great Britain ruled a huge empire overseas with its well-trained army.

The infantry advanced line by line. The first line would fire. Then, as the first reloaded their rifles, the next line would advance and fire. Keeping up a steady fire in this way, the troops advanced until they were close enough to charge the enemy with fixed bayonets. A bayonet was a long, knife-like blade that fitted on to the end of a rifle.

Many soldiers died in such attacks. Their colourful uniforms were easy targets for the enemy. So, by the end of the 1800s, dull khaki uniforms had replaced the bright red coats of the 'thin red line.'

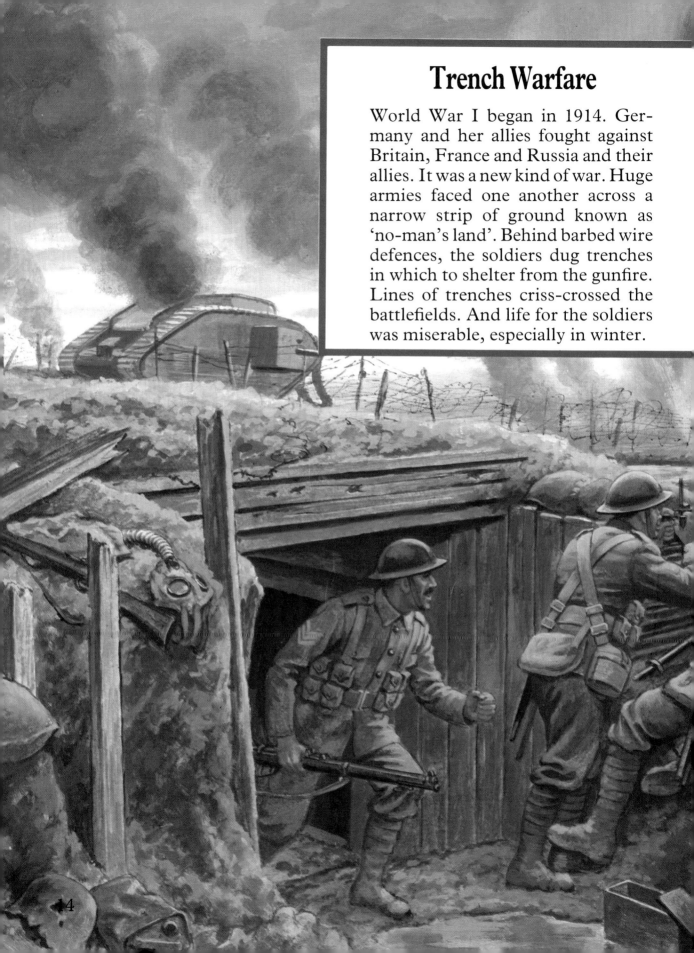

Trench Warfare

World War I began in 1914. Germany and her allies fought against Britain, France and Russia and their allies. It was a new kind of war. Huge armies faced one another across a narrow strip of ground known as 'no-man's land'. Behind barbed wire defences, the soldiers dug trenches in which to shelter from the gunfire. Lines of trenches criss-crossed the battlefields. And life for the soldiers was miserable, especially in winter.

Before an attack, heavy guns fired thousands of high explosive shells at the enemy lines. The shells left deep holes everywhere and churned the ground into mud. Then the infantry charged out of the trenches. They wore steel helmets and carried rifles and hand grenades. Often they fought hand-to-hand with bayonets.

After each attack, thousands more soldiers lay dead. both sides fought bravely, but seldom won more than a few hundred metres of ground.

The quick-firing machine guns made the old style of infantry and cavalry warfare impossible. They could mow down troops and horses in seconds. Horses were replaced by armoured cars, trucks, and later, tanks. For the first time, aeroplanes flew over the lines.

In 1918 the Allies, helped by American troops, broke through at last, and World War I was over. More than eight million men had lost their lives. Never again would people think of war as an exciting adventure.

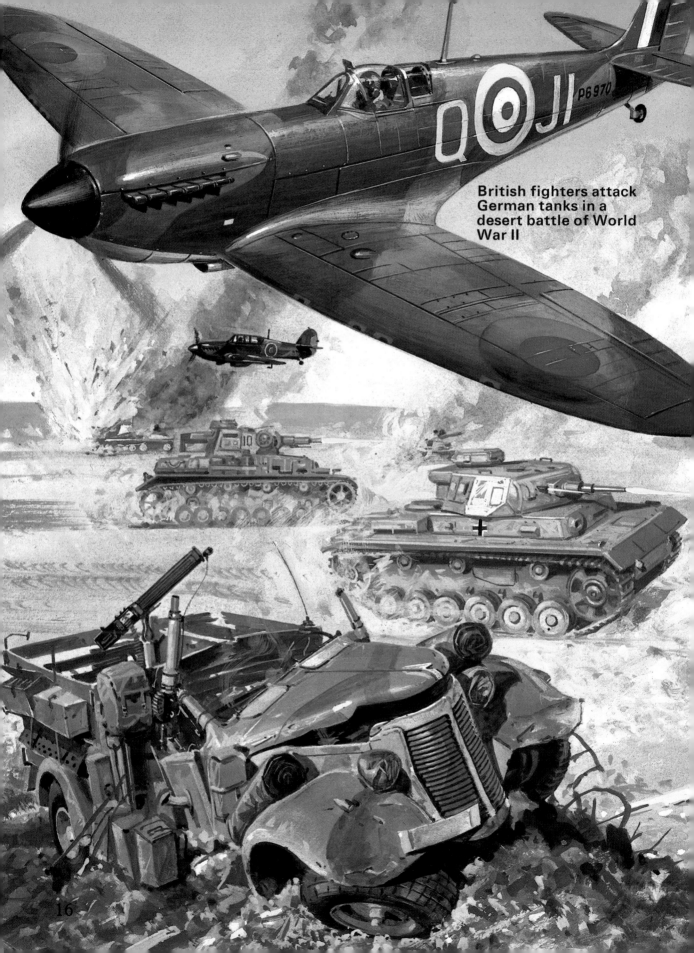

British fighters attack German tanks in a desert battle of World War II

Night air-raid in World War II

Tanks and Planes

People thought World War I had been 'the war to end all wars'. But in 1939 another great war, World War II, began.

In this war, the most deadly weapons on land were tanks. And fighter and bomber planes ruled in the air. The Germans used these weapons in their 'blitzkrieg' or 'lightning war' attacks. First they 'softened up' their target with bombing raids. Then the armies followed, driving their armoured vehicles across country at high speed.

In North Africa and Russia hundreds of tanks, armoured cars and guns took part in land battles. The tanks ran on caterpillar tracks to help them cross rough ground. They had powerful guns mounted in turrets and thick steel armour to protect the men inside.

One of the most important battles of World War II was fought in the air. This was the Battle of Britain in 1940. The fighters of the Royal Air Force defeated the attacks of the heavy German bombers, and so stopped Germany from invading Britain.

Both sides used bombers in air raids, killing many people and destroying whole towns. Barrage balloons floating on long cables were one defence. They burst into flames when they were hit. At night searchlights swept the sky, picking out enemy bombers. Lit up against the night sky, the bombers were then clear targets for ground-mounted anti-aircraft guns.

War at Sea

The first sea battles were fought in ancient times. The Persians, Greeks and Romans had warships called galleys with sails and oars. In battle, the ships tried to ram each other. Galley slaves rowed as fast as possible, crashing into enemy ships to damage them so that they sank.

Outside the Mediterranean, the seas were too rough for galleys. In the Middle Ages, some warships looked like floating castles, with raised decks at each end crowded with soldiers.

A great change came with the invention of guns. Handsome wooden galleons tried to sail faster than the enemy and fire 'broadsides' from their rows of cannon. In 1588 the faster English ships defeated the large, clumsy galleons of the Spanish Armada. The last great battle between wooden sailing ships, or 'men-of-war', was in 1805 at Trafalgar, off Spain, when a British fleet

defeated the French and Spanish. During the 1800s steam engines replaced sails, and armoured battleships known as 'ironclads' appeared. Their guns were mounted in revolving turrets and fired exploding shells.

In this century, battleships, destroyers, and aircraft carriers have fought battles far from land. Submarines, some now armed with nuclear missiles, were also added to warfare at sea.

mushroom cloud
nuclear explosion

V-1 'flying bomb'

missile-carrying nuclear submarine

20

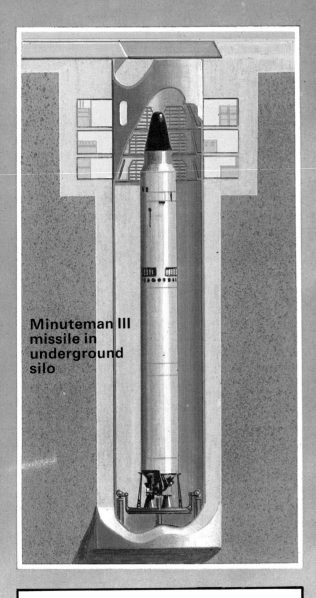

Minuteman III
missile in
underground
silo

Missiles are hidden underground in concrete silos to make it more difficult for an enemy to find and destroy them. They can also be fired from submarines beneath the sea. Nuclear-powered missile-carrying submarines can stay underwater for weeks at a time.

When a nuclear bomb explodes, a huge mushroom cloud rises high into the air. The blast, heat and radioactive fallout produced by such an explosion destroys all life over a huge area.

The Missile Age

Rockets were first used by the Chinese as weapons as well as fireworks. But after guns were invented, rockets were not often used in war until modern times. Today, guided missiles – large rockets carrying nuclear bombs – are the most terrible of all weapons.

The first 'flying bomb' was the V-1. Used by Germany in World War II, it was a small, pilotless aircraft with a jet engine. Inside it was packed with explosives. After launching, the V-1 flew towards its target. After a set time its motor stopped. Then it fell to earth and exploded.

The V-1 was followed by the V-2, a bigger, faster, rocket-powered missile. After the war, the V-2 was copied by the Americans and the Russians. New rockets were built. Some were used to explore space, others to carry nuclear weapons.

The first atomic bombs, dropped on two Japanese cities in 1945, were carried by aircraft. To carry the much more powerful hydrogen bomb, long-range ballistic missiles were built. These large rockets have several motors. They work in stages and fly so fast that they can cross continents in minutes. The bomb or 'warhead' is carried in the nose. Some missiles can carry several warheads, each one guided electronically to a different target.

1 Greek warrior, 400s BC

2 Roman centurion, 100s AD

3 Norman knight, 1066

4 German knight, 1400s

5 English soldier in Cromwell's New Model Army, 1645

6 British private, 60th Foot Regiment, 1757

7 Grenadier, French Imperial Guard, 1804

8 Enlisted man, US Federal Infantry, 1861

9 Lancer, British 17th Lancers, 1800s

10 Private, German 10th Württemberg Infantry Regiment, 1914

11 Private First Class, US Infantry, 1944

First published in Great Britain in 2014 by Osprey Publishing,
Kemp House, Chawley Park, Cumnor Hill, Oxford, OX2 9PH, UK
4301 21st. St., Suite 220, Long Island City, NY 11101, USA
E-mail: info@ospreypublishing.com

Osprey Publishing is part of the Osprey Group

A CIP catalog record for this book is available from the British Library

Print ISBN: 978 1 4728 0128 9
PDF e-book ISBN: 978 1 4728 0129 6
EPUB e-book ISBN: 978 1 4728 0130 2

Typeset in Garamond Pro and Myriad Pro

Originated by PDQ Media, Bungay, UK
Printed in China through Asia Pacific Offset Limited

14 15 16 17 18 10 9 8 7 6 5 4 3 2 1

Osprey Publishing is supporting the Woodland Trust, the UK's leading woodland conservation
charity, by funding the dedication of trees.

www.ospreypublishing.com

Dedication
To Maya Sheppard;
My Athena
My Artemis
My Grey-Eyed Girl
My Daughter

CONTENTS

INTRODUCTION

"Rage – goddess, sing the rage of Peleus' son, Achilles." These words, from the translation by Robert Fagles, introduce Homer's *Iliad*, the foundation text of western literature. Though set in a Bronze Age world over three millennia ago, the theme it explores – the price we pay for love and hate alike – resonates through time, for the conflicting obligations of power, honour, desire, duty, and family, are universal to the human experience. There is no stark definition of black and white in the struggle over Helen of Troy. Every character has plausible motivations. It is impossible not to sympathise with, and at the same time be critical of, all the players involved. That is the way of things; no-one is ever absolutely right or wrong. From such conflict even victory long hungered for tastes bittersweet.

TROY – FACT OR FICTION?

Lost to time, Troy passed from history into legend. Few placed much credence in German archaeologist Heinrich Schliemann when he began excavations at the mound of Hisarlik in 1871. But he found Troy, or, more accurately, many Troys, layered one on top of the other. Which – if any – was Priam's city? There is general agreement with the conclusion of Wilhelm Dörpfeld that Troy VI, sublevel h, is the most likely candidate. Although much of what was left of the sixth settlement was destroyed in the course of Schliemann's excavations, enough of it survives to indicate that it represents the most flourishing phase of Troy's existence, extending over a period of several hundred years in the second millennium before ending abruptly sometime around the middle of the thirteenth century BC. The remains of the great northeast bastion from this level calls to mind Homer's imposing watchtower. The distinctive slope in Troy VIh's walls lends credibility to the account in the *Iliad* of Patroclus' attempts to scale the fortifications.

Tantalizing clues have also been found in the records of Anatolia's Bronze Age superpower, the Hittite Empire. A reference is made around 1400 BC to a rebellion comprising twenty-two subject peoples, who apparently formed a confederacy, including the names Wilusiya and Taruisa. Were these the Hittite way of writing the names (W)ilios (Ilios) and Troia (Troy)? We know the Hittites were in diplomatic contact with the Achaeans (whose land is called Ahhiyawa in Hittite texts), and there was tension between them over spheres of influence in the Aegean borderland. Did this incorporate a major combined-arms expedition by the Achaeans against the most strategically sited of the Hittite client states? The debate continues. But, whatever conclusions can be drawn about the historical roots of the Trojan War, the saga will forever stand alone.

The Thousand Ships

Forbidden Fruit

There came a time, in an Age of Bronze, when Zeus, the king of the gods, decided to relieve the all-nurturing Earth from the burden of men by causing the Trojan War, that the load of death might empty the world.

At the centre of these divine machinations, as with all great sagas, was a wedding. If the bride on this occasion, however, were blushing, it was only because her cheeks were flushed with anger. Her name was Thetis; she was a Nereid, a daughter of the ancient sea god Nereus. She had accepted the rule of the new gods, the children of Cronus, who ruled from Mt. Olympus, but balancing the rivalry of these tempestuous deities was an unceasing challenge. To please Hera, reigning queen of Olympus, Thetis had spurned the attentions of her husband, Zeus. Enraged, he had sworn that she would be the wife of a mortal, Peleus of Phthia. Their wedding was staged on Mt. Pelion, where Apollo played the lyre and the Muses sang. All high society, human and divine, was there to celebrate the occasion, except Eris, the goddess of discord, who, for obvious reasons, had been left off the guest list. Out of spite, she crashed the party and hurled a golden apple from the Garden of the Hesperides into its midst. On it were inscribed the corrosive words, "to the fairest." This poisonous fruit was immediately claimed by Hera, Athena, and Aphrodite. They appealed to Zeus for judgment but he, fearing to make two enemies to one ally however he ruled, demurred. As a substitute, he suggested a mortal. Paris, a young man who tended his father's flocks on the slopes of Mt. Ida, in the dominion of Troy.

Heralded by Hermes, the three goddesses presented themselves before Paris, each seeking to win his favour. Hera promised him power, rule over Europe and Asia. Athena offered him wisdom and prowess in battle. But Aphrodite tempted him with Helen of Sparta, the most beautiful woman in the world. The fact that she was a queen of another country and married, meant nothing to Paris. Aflame with passion, he declared Aphrodite the winner on the spot, yearning as he was to claim his prize and make her Helen of Troy.

Would Paris have rendered a different judgment had he known how it ensnared him in web of political rivalry and jealousy spanning three generations on both sides of the Aegean? Though he had no inkling of the truth, his lover, the nymph Oenone, did. Possessing the art of prophecy, she warned Paris not to pursue Helen. Failing in that, she urged him to come

(PREVIOUS PAGE)

She was Helen of Sparta before she was Helen of Troy. Gazing at the Horse being hauled into her adopted city, knowing full well what it portended, where did her loyalties lie – with her old home, or with the new? Should she betray the warriors secreted within its belly, or let fate take its course? There was no good option, as her conflicted response that evening displayed. The entire saga approached its crisis, and whatever the outcome, it could only add to her guilt, her self-loathing, for her ultimate responsibility.

to her if he were ever wounded, for she alone could heal him. But Paris, consumed with visions of a wider destiny, forsook her.

His fate, though he did not perceive it, was intimately bound up with that of the city of Troy, renowned as the jewel of the Aegean. Her strategic position at the mouth of the Hellespont endowed her with profit from the rich trade routes linking the Mediterranean with the Black Sea. She had fully recovered her prestige after the disastrous reign of the previous king, Laomedon, who had prevailed upon Poseidon to build the walls of the city, then reneged when the time came for payment. In his anger, Poseidon unleashed a sea monster against Troy, and to save his city, Laomedon had no choice but to

Where the trouble began; Heracles about to kill Laomedon, king of Troy. Behind the demigod stands the melancholy Hesione. Winning her back was the obsession of Laomedon's sole surviving heir, Priam. This set in motion the chain of events that culminated in the second fall of Troy. (PD)

offer his daughter, Hesione, as a sacrifice. At that moment, Heracles passed by, on his way to join Jason and the other heroes of the age (including Peleus and his brother Telamon, the king of Salamis) in their quest for the Golden Fleece. Heracles rescued the girl but was cheated of his reward by Laomedon. The enraged demigod assembled an army, sacked Troy, and, starting with Laomedon, slaughtered every male member of the royal family. The sole exception was prince Podarces, who saved his life by offering Heracles a golden veil crafted by Hesione. Henceforth, the prince would bear the name Priam, from *priamai*, "to buy," or *priatos*, "ransomed." Hesione was given as a prize to Telamon, but Heracles allowed her to redeem one of her fellow captives from slavery. She chose her brother, and Priam became Troy's new king.

Under his leadership, Troy amassed great wealth and emerged at the head of a regional alliance incorporating the surrounding kingdoms. Having done so much to revive his city and perpetuate his line, Priam was suddenly confronted with the legacy of a past he had thought closed forever.

Sheltering Helen beneath his shield with one hand and gesturing towards his ship with the other, Paris shoots his way out of Mycenae in this 18th century painting by Gavin Hamilton. (Pushkin Museum, Moscow, Russia / The Bridgeman Art Library)

The first son born to Priam's queen, Hecuba, was Hector, but when heavy with a second child she dreamed that she gave birth to a firebrand that consumed Troy in flames. When this vision was reported to the seers, they bade her slay whatever child she should bear to avoid it being the ruin of the country. When the babe was born, Priam gave it to a servant, Agelaus, to take and expose on Mt. Ida. Abandoned, the infant was nursed for five days by a she-bear. When Agelaus found the boy still alive, he bore him home to his farm and brought him up as his own son. Thus did the judgment of Paris come to be made by a prince of Troy, all unwitting of his true heritage.

It was after this affair that heralds from Troy came to Mt. Ida and in the name of Priam carried away Agelaus's prize bull. Paris escorted the beast, which was intended to serve as a trophy and a sacrifice at the climax of ritual games, to the city. But once there, he impulsively entered the contests himself and defeated everyone, even his own siblings, the princes of Troy. When the seer Cassandra identified Paris as her brother and the doom of the city, Priam acknowledged his paternity and, scorning the prophecy, received him into the palace.

The handsome and headstrong Paris quickly insinuated himself into the inner councils of state. Playing upon his father's longing to reunite the family by bringing home its last outstanding member, he prevailed upon Priam to dispatch him on a diplomatic mission to recover Hesione. This granted, he set sail for Achaea on fast vessels built by the master shipbuilder Phereclus. But Paris was bound for Sparta, not Salamis. Claiming his reward from Aphrodite consumed his mind, blinding him to the fact that his endeavour had geopolitical implications far beyond his personal quest.

Leda, the previous queen of Sparta, had borne two sons, the legendary hero twins Castor and Pollux. She also had two daughters, Clytemnestra by her husband, Tyndareus, and Helen by Zeus, who seduced her in the form of a swan. The marriages of both girls would prove tragic. Clytemnestra was claimed by Agamemnon, the king of Mycenae, as a trophy after he killed her first husband, Tantalus, and dashed their child's brains out before her eyes. When Helen came of age, her legendary beauty attracted a host of suitors, the greatest warlords of the age. Ajax, Diomedes, Patroclus, Idomeneus, and Agamemnon's brother, Menelaus, each came with extravagant gifts and hot tempers. These self-styled heroes lived by the rule of *arête*, the pursuit of excellence. Each aspired to achieve *aristeia*, the great moment in battle that would define their place in history. Their rivalry for the hand of Helen threatened to drown Achaea in blood. The way out was offered by Odysseus, who had little hope of winning the prize himself. Odysseus proposed that every suitor should swear an oath requiring that each would come to the aid of whomsoever won Helen's hand should any other man seek to deprive the victor of his bride. This done, Helen was free to make her choice. Her heart was set on Menelaus, who settled in Sparta and inherited the kingdom from Tyndareus.

This was the state of affairs when Paris arrived, clad, in Euripides' evocative phrase, "in robes of gorgeous hue, ablaze with gold, in true barbaric pomp." For nine days he was entertained by Menelaus, but on the tenth day, the king was summoned to Crete to perform the funeral rites of his grandfather, Catreus. In her husband's absence, Paris persuaded Helen to elope with him. Abandoning her nine-year-old daughter, Hermione, and having stashed the kingdom's treasure on board, she set sail for Troy that night.

Contrary winds drove the lovers first to Egypt, then to Cyprus. Having obtained more ships there, Paris made for Phoenicia, where the king of Sidon received him kindly. That night, the Trojan prince treacherously murdered his host and pillaged the palace. Having stirred up a hornets nest, Paris was lucky to escape, losing two ships in the process. Upon his return home, Priam's horror at being presented with Helen instead of Hesione was soothed when the treasures of two royal houses were added to that of Troy.

The Warlords Assemble

Menelaus, meanwhile, had appealed to his brother Agamemnon, who seized upon this affront to his family's honour as a means of bringing all Achaea under his sway. Drawing upon their oaths, he summoned the other warlords to an assembly at Argos to strategize a combined front against Troy. Each man pledged to marshal his forces for war and send them to the rendezvous at Aulis in Boeotia.

Despite their oath, some of the key players were missing from this conclave. Chief among them, ironically, was Odysseus himself. Having been forewarned that if he departed for the war he would only return home after two decades of trial, he feigned madness as a means to escape his obligation. When Agamemnon and his entourage arrived, they found the king of Ithaca, having yoked an ass to an ox, ploughing his native soil with salt. This charade might have succeeded had Agamemnon's cousin Palamedes, Odysseus's only rival among the Achaeans in terms of craft and cunning, not taken the king's infant son, Telemachus, and placed him in the path of the plough. When Odysseus reined in his team his deception was exposed. He had no choice but to bid farewell to his beloved wife Penelope and embark for Aulis.

Having been drafted himself, Odysseus was only too eager to ensure that no others escaped the summons to war. His direst expectations were confirmed at Aulis when the seer Calchas noted a snake attacking a bird's nest. The intruder devoured the eight chicks and, finally, the mother. In this was a sign; the struggle against Troy would consume nine years. Only in the tenth would the Achaeans achieve victory.

Calchas also prophesied that Troy could not be taken without Achilles, the son of Thetis and Peleus. Achaea's cause was lost without its greatest warrior, but he was nowhere to be found. His mother had foreseen two possible fates for him: a long, happy life ignored by history should he stay home, or a short, turbulent life that would pass into legend should he enlist for the war against

Troy. Dreading the latter, she disguised him in female garb and entrusted him as a maiden to Lycomedes of Skyros, who had many daughters. The girls called him Pyrrha for his tawny hair, but his true nature led to a secret affair with the king's oldest daughter, Deidameia, who bore him a son called Neoptolemus.

The subterfuge held until Odysseus and Diomedes, combing the Aegean islands for his whereabouts, arrived at Skyros. Suspecting the truth, Odysseus contrived to present the court with gifts suitable for young maidens. He included amidst the baubles and finery a sword and spear. When Diomedes staged an assault on the throne room, Achilles instinctively seized the weapons to defend the court. His disguise exposed, he willingly accepted the path of the warrior and the endeavour against Troy. Along with his family retainers, the Myrmidon warriors, he was accompanied by Phoenix, king of the Dolopians, an old associate of his father, and his cousin Patroclus, the son of Polymele, daughter of Peleus.

Not every effort to raise allies bore fruit. King Cinyras of Cyprus swore he would send fifty ships, but in the event, dispatched only one, commanded by his son, Mygdalion. In mocking fulfilment of his father's obligation,

FRIEND & FOE

For all of the attention it lavishes on the hyper-masculine qualities of honour, pride, and the martial arts, the central character of the Trojan saga remains a woman, Helen. Her infidelity, much as she might come to bitterly regret it, was the spark that ignited the war. But there were deeper imperatives at stake for the two Atreidae, the sons of Atreus, Agamemnon and Menelaus. While the former, the elder brother, had inherited the throne of Mycenae, the younger brother was only king of Sparta by marriage. Helen's elopement thus threatened the family's consolidation of power in what is now Greece (which, during the Bronze Age, did not exist even as a concept. The peoples living there were loosely defined by the two richest kingdoms as either Achaeans or Argives).

Three generations of warlords rallied to the cause of the Atreidae, from youths like Achilles, to mature men like Diomedes, Idomeneus and Odysseus, who left young families at home, to veterans like Nestor, who brought their adult sons to war with them. The motivations of these men were as varied as their ages and ancestry. Obligation, opportunism, greed, and glory all impelled them to take up arms. For some, the ties of blood made

for conflicted loyalties. Amongst those answering the call was Ajax the Greater of Salamis (to avoid confusion, Ajax the Lesser of Locris is hereby referred to by the alternate spelling of his name, Aias). Ironically, while Ajax was the son of Telamon and Periboea, his half-brother Teucer was the son of Telamon and Priam's sister Hesione, making him cousin to the very princes of Troy he was destined to cross swords with.

As king of Troy, Priam sired dozens of bastards by his concubines, but only those children by his wife qualified to enter the elite circle of the royal family. Hecuba's firstborn was Hector, and after him Paris. She bore Priam ten more sons (Deiphobus, Helenus, Polydorus, Troilus, Polites, Antiphus, Pammon, Hipponous, Dius, and Agathon) and six daughters (Iliona, Cassandra, Laodice, Creusa, Philomela, and Polyxena). Cassandra was a seer, though her gift came at a bitter price. Apollo had granted her the art of prophecy, but when she refused to surrender her favours in return, the god laid a curse that she could persuade no-one of the truth revealed in her visions, not even when the doom of her city was literally at the gates.

the prince launched forty-nine model vessels, moulded out of Cyprian clay, into the waters off Aulis.

When the armada was finally assembled and ready to sail, Agamemnon shot a stag within the groves of a temple to Artemis, compounding his error by boasting of his prowess at hunting being greater than hers. In response, the spiteful goddess sent contrary winds that kept every vessel pinned to the shore. As days turned into weeks of inactivity, with its attendant threats of hunger and disease, the entire enterprise threatened to unravel before it even embarked for Troy.

The desperate Agamemnon consulted Calchas as to how he might appease the immortals. The seer's reply shocked him to the core. Artemis would be satisfied with nothing less than the sacrifice of Agamemnon's own daughter, Iphigenia.

Odysseus and Diomedes were dispatched to Mycenae and ordered to return to Aulis with Iphigenia on the pretext that she was to marry Achilles. At the last moment, Menelaus lost heart and urged his brother to abandon the entire enterprise, but by then it was too late. According to Euripides, Agamemnon genuinely feared being "left wasting, night and day, in sorrow for what I did to one of my own flesh and blood, contrary to all law and justice." But he could not send his daughter back to Mycenae because Calchas would inform the army of his refusal. That couldn't happen if the seer were disposed of first, Menelaus assured him, "an easy matter." Not so, Agamemnon replied,

The Sacrifice of Iphigenia, as rendered by the 18th century artist Giovanni Battista Tiepolo. According to some accounts, the goddess Artemis, impressed by the courage of the maid, substituted a stag in her place on the altar. (Bridgeman Art Library)

Helen of Troy by José Daniel
Cabrera Peña

for Odysseus knew all. The brothers agreed this represented the true threat
to their position, for the king of Ithaca, "ever shifty by nature, siding with
the mob," was "enslaved by the love of popularity, a fearful evil." Should
Agamemnon fail to lead the army, Odysseus would take it away from him, and
even if the high king did escape to Argos, his erstwhile subjects would run him
to ground there and storm the walls of his palace. In his absence, Iphigenia
would still be sacrificed and the expedition against Troy would still go forward.

PAPHLAGONIA
⚔ Pylaemenes

AMAZONIA
⚔ Penthesilea →

HALIZONIA
⚔ Epistrophus →
⚔ Odius

ETHIOPIA
⚔ Memnon →

CYPRUS
Mygdalion →

50 miles

0

50km

0

PHYRGIA
⚔ Asius

LYCIA
⚔ Glaucus
⚔ Sarpedon

THRACE
⚔ Acamas
⚔ Piras
⚔ Rhesus

● Percote
⚔ Asius
⚔ Adrestus
⚔ Amphius
Sestos

● Pandarus

Mt. Ida ▲
⚔ Eetion
Lymessus
● Mynes

MYSIA
⚔ Chromius
⚔ Ennomus
⚔ Eurypylus

TROAD
Troy ⚔ Hector
⚔ Paris
⚔ Deiphobus
⚔ Cycnus ⚔ Aeneas
⚔ Archelochus

CARIA

LYDIA

MAEONIA
⚔ Hipothous
⚔ Pylaeus
Smyrna

● Phocaea
● Colophon

Methlis
Antiphus

⚔ Nastes
⚔ Amphimacus

COS
Phidippus
Antiphus

RHODES
⚔ Tlepolemus

SYME
⚔ Nireus

THRACE

SAMOTHRACE

IMBROS

LESBOS

CHIOS

SAMOS

CARPATHOS

THASOS

⚔ Euphemus

LEMNOS

TENEDOS

AEGEAN SEA

Neoptolemus
SKYROS

MYKONOS

NAXOS

THERA

ANDROS

TENOS

CRETE
Knossos ●
Idomeneus
Meriones

PAEONIA
⚔ Pyraechemes
⚔ Asteropaeus

Mt. Olympus ▲
● Polypoetes
Leonteus
Guneus

● Podalirius
⚔ Machaon

Prothous
Eurypylus
● Medon

Pylace
● Eumelus
● Pherae
⚔ Podarces
⚔ Protesilaus
⚔ Achilles
⚔ Patroclus
⚔ Phoenix

● Philoctetes

⚔ Ialmenus
⚔ Ascalaphus
Delphi
⚔ Alas
PHOCIS
LOCRIS
⚔ Schedius BOEOTIA Thebes
Epistrophus ● Aulis
⚔ Arcesilaus
⚔ Clonius Leitus
⚔ Prothoenor
⚔ Peneleus

EUBOEA
⚔ Elephenor
⚔ Thersander

Menestheus
ATTICA
● Athens

AETOLIA
⚔ Amphimacus
Thalpius
Polyxenus
⚔ Diares
Thoas

● Meges

● Eurytus

Odysseus ●

ITHACA
CEPHALLENIA

ZACYNTHUS

ACHAEA
⚔ Agamemnon
⚔ Adrastus
Amaryncus
Argos ●
Agapenor
ARCADIA

Mycenae
SALAMIS
⚔ Ajax
Teucer
⚔ Palamedes
⚔ Diomedes
Eurylaus
Sthenelus
Cyanippus
ARGOLIS

LACONIA
● Sparta
Menelaus
⚔ Antiochus
⚔ Thrasymedes
Gerenia
● Nestor

CYTHERA

IONIAN SEA

CORCYRA

● Achaean City
● Trojan City
PAEONIA States
THASOS Islands
Hector Warlords
⚔ Warlord who never
made it home alive
after the fall of Troy

Unexpectedly, Clytemnestra arrived with the bridal party, intending to take charge of the nuptial arrangements. When the truth was uncovered, her horror at the intended fate of her daughter was matched only by Achilles' outrage at his unwitting part in this deception. But in this he was alone. No-one would stand by him, not even his own Myrmidon warriors. There was no way out. If Agamemnon ordered his daughter sacrificed, the army would come for her, with Odysseus at its head. Nonetheless, his honour compelled him to take on every Achaean in arms, if necessary, for the sake of this one life, though it meant his own doom.

The affair was on the brink of spiralling out of control when Iphigenia, for the sake of Achilles' life, her father's reputation, and the greater glory of Achaea, voluntarily surrendered herself to the knife. "This is my enduring monument," she stated, in Euripides' epic phrase; "marriage, motherhood, and fame – all these is it to me."

Thus did Agamemnon exchange his own daughter for command over a great host of warriors. However, this episode lost him the respect of Achilles and the loyalty of his wife. The former would nearly cost him the war; the latter would ultimately cost him his life.

Gods & Goddesses

The Olympian gods were a constant, and physical, presence in the time of Helen. She herself was a daughter of Zeus. He came to her mother, Leda, in the form of a swan, and their offspring was hatched from an egg. Many other figures from antiquity proudly claimed lineage from the union of the human and the celestial. Sometimes this worked in their favour; for example, divine intervention rescued Aeneas, the son of Aphrodite, from certain death on multiple occasions. Others were abandoned to their fate. Sarpedon, the son of Zeus; Penthesilea, the daughter of Ares; Memnon, the son of Eos; and Achilles, the son of Thetis; all fell in battle before the end of the war.

The capricious quality of the immortals is a constant throughout the sagas. In the *Iliad*, Zeus might boast, "how far I tower over the gods, I tower over men." But his status as king of the gods in many ways paralleled that of Agamemnon, the king of kings. Each was first amongst equals. Their rule relied upon status, and

the fiercely independent spirits under their ostensible authority were always chafing against the obligations imposed upon them. Despite Zeus making clear his injunction against interference in the struggle over Helen, the other immortals incessantly interceded on behalf of one side or the other. The following table lists the favouritism of the gods.

FOR THE ACHAEANS

Hera: sister and wife of Zeus, queen of Olympus
Athena: daughter of Zeus and Metis, goddess of wisdom
Poseidon: brother of Zeus, god of the sea
Hephaestus: son of Zeus and Hera, god of the forge

FOR THE TROJANS

Aphrodite: daughter of Zeus and Dione, goddess of love
Apollo: son of Zeus and Leto, god of art and archery
Artemis: daughter of Zeus and Leto, goddess of the hunt
Ares: son of Zeus and Hera, god of war

Black Ships Bound For Troy

The advent of favourable winds, bought at so terrible a price, enabled the Achaeans to set sail for Troy. En route the expeditionary force washed up on the shores of Mysia and found itself drawn into a war with king Telephus, a tall and powerful man whose deeds of valour rivalled those of his divine father, Heracles. With the Achaeans wavering, Achilles and Ajax divided the army between them and drove headlong into the fray. Ajax struck down Teuthranius, the half-brother of Telephus; enraged, the king threw himself against, and broke, the Achaean line, killing Thersander, the king of Thebes. Having mastered the battlefield, Telephus was in pursuit of Odysseus when Achilles hurled his spear and pierced the king's left thigh, forcing him to withdraw.

For all the ruin she brought to his city and to his household, Priam never seems to have lost the affection he bore for his daughter-in-law or regretted his decision to make her Helen of Troy. When the armies assembled on the plain he bade her, his dear child, sit before him and point out the Achaean heroes massing under the walls. Illustration by H. J. Ford.

The Achaean elite brought many assets to the endeavour against Troy: youthful vigour and wise maturity, strength and speed, guile and brute force. In a coalition of kings, however, the most critical trait of all – the binding force of authority – was always tenuous at best. Nominally under the supreme command of Agamemnon, the private feuds of these proud and jealous warlords might erupt at any moment with fatal consequences for the entire war effort.

Stalemated on the battlefield, the Achaeans resorted to diplomacy, approaching Telephus to open negotiations. The king instisted that Achilles be brought to him. Tormented by his wound, Telephus had been advised that he could only be healed by that which struck him. Achilles insisted that he had no such skill, but Odysseus pointed out that it was the spear, not the wielder, that was responsible for the king's suffering. When Achilles scraped flakes of the weapon into the wound, it was healed. The Achaeans urged Telephus to join them in the campaign against Troy, but he was willing to offer no more than guides and safe passage through his kingdom, for his wife Laodice, the mother of his son Eurypylus, was one of Priam's daughters.

The Achaeans had one more misadventure before arriving at their fated destination. Approaching the Hellespont, they prevailed upon Philoctetes to guide them to the sanctuary of Chryse on the island of Lemnos, where Heracles had made sacrifices prior to his own assault on Troy. As a boy, Philoctetes had accompanied Heracles on this expedition. Later, he had been the one who had lit the flames when Heracles, tormented unto madness by the shirt of Nessus, begged for his funeral pyre to be ignited. As a reward, Heracles had bequeathed Philoctetes his bow and unerring, envenomed arrows. They would eventually play a key role in the second fall of Troy, but while leading his comrades to the sanctuary, Philoctetes encountered a serpent, which plunged its fangs into his ankle. The poison rotted the wound, causing intense pain. The stench, and Philoctetes' frenzied cursing, was more than the Achaeans could bear. They slipped away to their ships and set sail, abandoning Philoctetes to his fate.

Now, at last, the Achaean armada arrived at the plain of Ilium beneath the walls of Troy. As the ships drew near to the shore, the warlords on board hesitated, for an oracle had warned that the first man of their company to touch Trojan soil would die. As the others vacillated, Protesilaus leapt from his ship. He was immediately killed by Hector, but his sacrifice freed the other Achaean warlords to storm ashore.

When Cycnus, a son of Poseidon, was killed by Achilles, the Trojans retreated to their city. The Achaeans were able to consolidate their beachhead, Achilles and Ajax being stationed at each end of the line to cover the flanks. The stretch of beach, broad as it was, could not offer berths to all of that massed armada. The troops, crammed into a narrow strip of coast, hauled their vessels inland, row upon row. Aware of the vulnerability this entailed, the Achaeans constructed a stockade wall masked by a stake-lined trench to keep the Trojans at bay.

There was a final attempt to arrive at a negotiated solution. Palamedes, Odysseus, and Menelaus were dispatched in an embassy to king Priam, but their arguments were in vain. Troy would not surrender Helen. After the ambassadors returned, empty-handed, both sides settled down for the inevitable siege. Since the Achaeans couldn't tighten the noose enough to effectively isolate Troy from the outside world, and the Trojans lacked the

PATROCLUS

ACHILLES

TEUCER

AJAX
THE GREAT

AGAMEMNON

DIOMEDES

ODYSSEUS

NESTOR

MENELAUS

The Achaean Forces

Although sharing a common language and culture that extended throughout the territory now claimed by the modern state of Greece, there was no singular Achaean nation at the time of the Trojan War. The land was divided up among numerous principalities, some rivals, others bound together by ties of kinship. Although recognizing Agamemnon as high king, each of the warlords under his overall command jealously upheld the right to significant autonomy. Decisions had to be reached by consensus. Whenever Agamemnon overstepped those bounds the backlash could be costly, as in his feud with Achilles. In battle, the rank and file fought best when shoulder to shoulder in their own clan, tribal, and provincial arrays.

Although all Achaea was mobilized, not every contribution was held of equal account. Homer details the number of ships committed to the campaign by each of the Achaean warlords. The following chart includes those, such as Thersander and Palamedes, who did not survive to be listed in the Iliad.

An expedition on this scale would have demanded significant logistical infrastructure to maintain such a massive army in the field for an extended period. There is a glimpse of this in Homer when Nestor remarks to Agamemnon, "Your shelters overflow with the wine Achaean ships bring in from Thrace, daily." The expedition would also have included its share of craftsmen, sutlers, stewards, and medical personnel to support the front line fighters. This is the less glamorous side to the saga, but it establishes a thread of continuity between the military endeavours of legend and those of today.

WARLORD SHIPS

Thersander of Thebes; Arcesilaus, Prothoenor, Peneleus, Leitus, and Clonius of Boeotia	50
Ascalaphus and Ialmenus, sons of Ares, of Orchomenus	30
Schedius and Epistrophus of Phocis	40
Aias of Locris	40
Elphenor of Euboea	40
Menestheus of Athens	50
Ajax and Teucer of Salamis	12
Palamedes and Diomedes of Argolis	80
Agamemnon of Mycenae	100
Menelaus of Lacedaemon	60
Nestor of Gerenia	90
Agapenor of Arcadia	60
Amphimachus, Thalpius, Diōres and Polyxenus of Elis	40
Meges of Dulichion	40
Odysseus of Ithaca	12
Thoas of Aetolia	40
Idomeneus and Meriones of Crete	80
Tlepolemus, son of Heracles, of Rhodes	9
Nireus of Syme	3
Pheidippus and Antiphus of Cos	30
Achilles, son of Thetis	50
Protesilaus and Podarces of Phylace	40
Eumelus of Pherae	11
Philoctetes of Methona	7
Podalirius and Machaon, sons of Asclepius	30
Eurypylus of Ormenion	40
Polypoetes and Leonteus	40
Guneus of Cyphus	22
Prothous of Magnesia	40
Mopsus of Colophon	20
Calchas of Acarnania	20
Epeus of the Cyclades	30

strength to drive the Achaeans back into the sea, a stalemate ensued. As the years lengthened and frustrations on both sides mounted, internal tensions threatened to boil over. On the Achaean side, Odysseus, who had never forgiven Palamedes for exposing the ruse of his madness, had long plotted to kill him in revenge, and finally succeeded in framing him as a turncoat. Agamemnon, who delivered Palamedes up to be stoned to death by the entire army, was suspected of having shared in this plot, for Palamedes' appeal to the rank and file endangered his own supreme command.

If the Achaeans couldn't take Troy, they could devastate an ever-widening circle of surrounding city states. Ajax assaulted the Phrygians, killed their ruler, Teuthras, in single combat, razed his city and carried off his daughter, Tecmessa. In his first such foray, Achilles captured Priam's son Lycaon. He then attacked Lesbos and took it by storm, killing Phorbas, the king of the island, and carrying off his daughter, Diomedea, along with much booty. Achilles took many other cities, among them Lyrnessus. One of the prizes there was a woman of surpassing beauty named Briseis. Having lost her father, mother, three brothers, and husband at the hands of Achilles, she now became his slave.

The message that this would be a war without mercy or pity was brought brutally home when the seer Calchas, desperate to get his daughter, Cresseida, away from her lover, Priam's son Troilus, foretold the city would not fall until the Trojan prince was dead. Achilles therefore ambushed the youth and slew him on the altar of Apollo.

These depredations, whilst honing Achaean arms, enriching her warlords, and filling her granaries, laid the seeds of a crisis that nearly shattered their entire enterprise.

For such a pivotal figure in the western literary canon, the real Homer remains elusive. Was he the blind bard of popular convention, or a composite figure from the traditional oral transmission of folk history?

THE RAGE OF ACHILLES

The Arrows of Apollo

One of the girls taken captive during the Achaean raids was Chryseis, daughter
of Chryses, a priest of Apollo. Coming in supplication to Agamemnon's tent
and offering precious gifts in exchange, Chryses begged for her release. But,
although all ranks of the army urged Agamemnon to accept the ransom, he
contemptuously refused. The girl was a trophy, a prize taken in battle, and
only death would free her from service either at the loom or in the high king's
bed in Argos.

Cruelly rebuffed, Chryses appealed to his patron Apollo, begging him to send his arrows in exchange for a father's tears. The god responded by raining down on the Achaean camp the deadly shafts of plague. Man and beast alike succumbed, and the corpse fires burned on, with no end in sight.

On the tenth day, Achilles finally called all ranks to muster. He consulted Calchas, who divined the presence of Apollo behind the pandemic and urged that Chryseis be returned to her father. Agamemnon grudgingly complied, but his outraged pride demanded compensation. He settled on Briseis, the prize of Achilles. It was a deliberate provocation, intended to shame Achilles into submission. It backfired. Achillies swore, asking aloud why Agamemnon took the greatest treasure when it was he that bore the brunt of the fighting. Unwilling to tolerate this disgrace, Achilles vowed to return home.

Brushing aside offers of mediation, Achilles retired to his tents. When his mother offered solace Achilles insisted that she urge Zeus to take up the Trojan cause, so that they might rout the Achaeans and drive them back against their ships. By his absence he would prove his worth to the cause, so that even Agamemnon might learn a lesson in respect for those who served with him, not under him. And true to his word, he abstained from any further fighting, nursing his wounded pride in self-imposed exile, though the distant cries of battle left him in an insatiable anguish of bloodlust.

Perversely, Agamemnon chose this moment to indulge a gambit in reverse psychology. Enmeshed in the snare set by a divinely-inspired dream, which promised ultimate victory should his men prove worthy, he marshalled the army and, as a test of their loyalty, ordered them to cut and run, to sail home for their lands and families.

Taking their commander-in-chief at his word, the assembled ranks degenerated into a mass exodus of men only too glad to put the conflict behind them. The entire Achaean war effort would have evaporated then and there had the other warlords not rallied their contingents to the cause. Chief among them was Odysseus, who stripped Agamemnon of his father's royal sceptre and used it to confront the fleeing masses.

Speaking for the rank and file, who had nothing invested in the affairs of royalty, Thersites urged his comrades to abandon Agamemnon, to leave him wallowing in his plunder. It was Odysseus who restored order, first by dressing down Thersites verbally and then by beating him down with the sceptre.

Into Battle

The army was dragged back into line just in time to confront another sortie from the besieged city. The Trojans advanced, shouting their war cries in many different languages. By contrast, the Achaeans marched in silence, conserving their energy for the grim business of war. Odysseus and Nestor's fleet-footed son, Antilochus, led the right wing. Ajax and Diomedes led the left, and Aias and grizzled, grey-haired Idomeneus led the centre.

Achilles, his sword half drawn, is prevented from killing Agamemnon only by the intervention of Athena, who seizes him by the hair. "Down from the skies I come to check your rage if only you will yield," she urges. An 18th century fresco by Giovanni Battista Tiepolo. (The Art Archive / Alamy)

But before the armies could come to grips, Paris sprang from the Trojan ranks, a leopard skin gaudily slung across his shoulders. He issued an open challenge to single combat. Menelaus seized this opportunity and accepted the challenge. When Paris then tried to slink back into the Trojan lines, Hector browbeat him into standing up for his country, berating him for being such a disgrace to his father, family and city. Paris sought to deflect the criticism by frankly admitting that such criticism was not unfair, in fact nothing less than he deserved. But his confession was hollow, meaningless without the lesson learned.

Perfectly content to witness the two men responsible for the war fighting out their private grievances, both armies halted while Paris and Menelaus squared off, the winner bound to claim Helen. Menelaus cast his spear, which punched right through the centre of Paris' shield and ripped through his breastplate. Before Paris could recover, Menelaus was on him with his sword, shattering it on his adversary's helmet. Lunging at Paris, he grabbed his horsehair crest, swung him around, and began dragging him bodily towards the Achaean lines.

Paris was on the verge of being throttled by his own ox-hide chinstrap when Aphrodite intervened, whisking him off to the safety of Helen's bedchamber.

Enraged, Menelaus stalked like a wild beast up and down the lines, thirsting to consummate his victory over the young upstart who had so shamed him. None of the Trojans could point out Paris, though all would have been happy to do so, for all of them had lost brothers, and brothers-in arms, over the course of the war and despised the cocksure princeling they held responsible.

This hiatus caused consternation on Olympus, too. Hera, Troy's implacable foe, insisted the city not escape destruction on a technicality. Zeus growled in response that he would not consent to the ruin of his most favoured city unless Hera pledged in return that she would not intervene whenever he resolved to turn his wrath on some city loyal to her. The queen of the gods readily conceded, offering her three favourites – Argos, Sparta, and Mycenae – in exchange. He was free to burn them to the ground. If his pleasure was their destruction she would not intervene. So the gods trade in human lives.

Acting as agent provocateur, Athena slipped into the Trojan ranks disguised as Laodocus, a son of Priam's key advisor Antenor, seeking the archer Pandarus. Whispering of glory, she urged Pandarus to draw his bow against Menelaus. Having roused him to violate the truce, she deflected the shot she had incited into a glancing blow. Agamemnon ordered his battalions back into battle. In making his tactical dispositions, he lined up his least reliable units in the centre, where they'd be forced to fight. As to his elite warriors, he ordered them to hold the line and fight side-by-side.

The Achaean ranks fell silent as the two armies closed, while battle cries in many tongues rose up from the long Trojan lines. Finally the clash came, the great press of bodies grinding together, shield on shield, sword to sword. Amid the general carnage, the warlords on each side carved out space to meet in individual combat, as when Odysseus struck down one of Priam's bastard sons, Democoon, spearing him straight through one temple and out the other.

Pandarus loosed another shot that hit Diomedes in the right shoulder, but his driver, Sthenelus, sprang from his chariot and pulled the arrow clean through the wound. Restored by Athena, Diomedes ran rampant, slaying Astynous, Hyprion, Abas, Polyidus, and two of Priam's bastards, Echemmon and Chromius. Aeneas urged Pandarus to shoot Diomedes down, but his only response was to lament that his arrows, in wounding Menelaus and Diomedes, had only unleashed the fury of the Achaeans. Previously, the bow he had received from Apollo himself was his most prized possession, but now, if he lived long enough to return home, he vowed to break the bow apart and throw it in the fire.

Pandarus finally mounted up and, with Aeneas driving, spurred directly for Diomedes and Sthenelus. Pandarus cast his spear first. It penetrated Diomedes' shield but not his breastplate. Diomedes' return throw hit Pandarus flush in the face, the point tearing downwards through teeth, tongue and jaw to exit under his chin.

Gods and Men

As Pandarus' corpse pitched out of the chariot, Aeneas sprang after it. Diomedes caught him with a boulder, smashing the socket, tendons and flesh of his hip. The great fighter sank to his knees, bracing himself with one strong forearm planted against the earth, and the world went black as night before his eyes. Only the intervention of his mother, Aphrodite, saved his life. Diomedes, entirely unfazed at the prospect of challenging the immortals, slashed the point of his spear clean through her wrist. Shrieking, the goddess dropped Aeneas. It took another god, Apollo, to save him this second time. Still Diomedes refused to back off. Three times he charged Aeneas, in a frenzy to bring him down, and three times Apollo had to drive him back. The god finally forced the Achaean to withdraw before quitting the field himself with Aeneas.

Yet another Olympian sought to turn the tide, as Ares, wading into the fight, spurred the Trojans on. Sarpedon taunted Hector to show the same mettle, for it was Troy's allies who were doing the fighting for her. Insulted, Hector leapt from his chariot and, brandishing his two spears, went striding down his lines, driving his fighters into battle. Aeneas, healed by Leto and Aphrodite, returned to the fray, killing a pair of ranking Achaeans, Orsilochus and Crethon, sending them crashing down like two lofty pine trees.

The world of Ilium depicted in a stylized representation. In the foreground is the Achaean beachhead and its protective wall; beyond it, the river Scamander and the open plain that was the main theatre of battle; and, looming above them all, the mighty ramparts and towers of Troy herself.

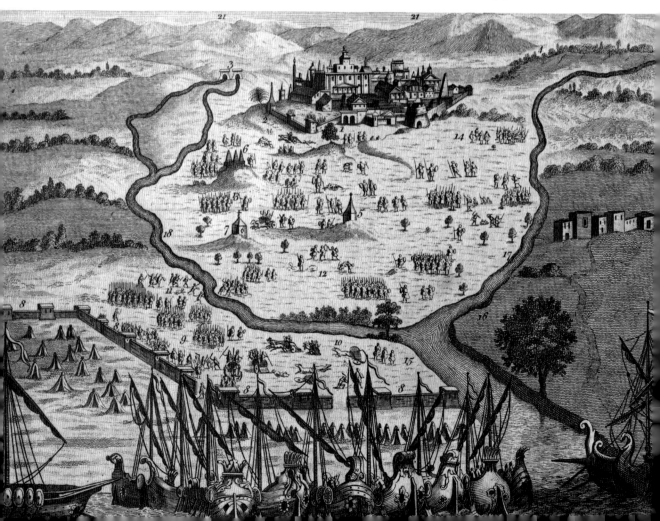

Menelaus and Antilochus then double-teamed Pylaemenes and his driver Mydon. While Menelaus struck down Pylaemenes, smashing his collarbone to splinters, Antilochus caught Mydon on the elbow with a rock and followed up with his sword. Tumbling from his chariot, Mydon plunged face first into the sand and was trampled to a pulp by his own horses.

Hector, lunging, levelled a pair of men, Menesthes and Anchialus, riding the same chariot. Ajax meanwhile struck down Amphius, but as he rushed to strip the armour he found himself surrounded by a swarm of Trojans hurling spears at him. His shield taking repeated hits, he dug his heel into the corpse to wrench out his own spear and was able to make good his escape.

Elsewhere, Tlepolemus of the Achaeans, a son of Heracles, took on Sarpedon, a son of Zeus, who fought for Troy. Each hurled his spear at the same moment. Sarpedon transfixed Tlepolemus through the neck, but in return took his adversary's shaft in the left thigh and had to be borne from the field.

Ares and Hector between them mowed down Teuthras, Orestes, Trechus, Oenomaus, Helenus, and Oresbius. Hera and Athena now directly intervened, Hera rallying the Achaean ranks, Athena flicking Sthenelus out of his chariot and seizing the reins herself to commit Diomedes against Ares. The war god was stripping the armour from his most recent victim, giant Periphas, the Aetolians' best fighter, when he noticed Diomedes closing in. He hurled his spear, but Athena deflected it, and Diomedes' shaft struck home, burying itself deep in Ares' bowels. The Olympian let out a bellow of pain so intense it brought the combatants on both sides to a stunned silence. Limping back to Olympus, Ares bewailed the affront to his father, but Zeus had no sympathy for his son's whining, hating him as he did most of all the gods for having inherited his mother's uncontrollable rage.

With Ares gone, the Achaeans rallied. Menelaus caught Adrestus alive after his horses snared his chariot in tamarisk branches and tore it apart. Adrestus clutched Menelaus' knees and begged for mercy, pleading for him to take the treasure piled up in his wealthy father's house in exchange for his life. Menelaus was about to hand him off to take back to the ships when Agamemnon intervened, pledging total destruction of Troy, down to the babes yet unborn in their mothers' wombs. Menelaus thus pushed Adrestus aside, and Agamemnon stabbed him in the flank. The high king then dug a heel on his still heaving chest and contemptuously tore his spear free.

The bonds of hospitality ruled elsewhere on the battlefield. When Glaucus and Diomedes encountered each other in no-man's-land, they discovered that they had a shared heritage in that Glaucus' grandfather, Bellerophon, was a close friend of Diomedes' grandfather Oeneus. Pledging mutual guarantees of safe conduct, the two fighters plunged their spears in the ground and exchanged armour as a token of their friendship. After all, Diomedes noted, there were plenty of other Trojans for him to kill and no shortage of Achaeans too.

At this juncture, Priam's son Helenus, greatest of the Trojan seers, urged Hector to return to the city and instruct their mother, Hecuba, to lead an appeal to Athena. While on this assignment, Hector found Paris lounging in the palace and subjected his brother to another tongue lashing. When Paris still failed to move, Hector turned to Helen to see if she could motivate his brother. Helen just shook her head, saying she wished she was the wife of a better man

Disgusted, Hector left them to spend a few precious moments with his wife and child before returning to the grim business of war. He found them at the Scaean Gates. Andromache had already lost her father and her seven brothers to the conflict raging outside the walls. They had been cut down by Achilles when he stormed their Cilician city. Orphaned by the Achaeans, she had no desire that they render her a widow. Andromache urged Hector to remain within the city before his own fiery courage destroyed him. Her bereavement should he fall in battle weighed on his mind constantly, but his domestic concerns were outweighed by his obligation to the warrior code, for he would be unable to face the men fighting and dying for Troy should he shrink from battle now and be labelled a coward.

Hector reached for his son, Astyanax, but the boy recoiled, clinging against his nurse's breast, terrified by his father's flashing bronze helmet with its bristling horsehair crest. Hector and Andromache both laughed, lost in the moment. Hector set down his helmet and raised his son in his arms, praying that one day he would be celebrated as a better man than his father. Then he placed Astyanax in Andromache's arms, reassuring her that he was not fated to fall that day, and turned back to the battle.

This late 5th century BC Attic terracotta cup, made by the potter Kaliades and painted by Douris, portrays the duel between Ajax and Hector, depicting the moment when Hector's knees buckled under his foes' assault, and he fell flat on his back, his shield crashing down on him. (The Art Archive / Alamy)

As Andromache tearfully returned to her loom, Paris finally arrived, clad in characteristically gorgeous, glittering armour, his mood buoyant to match. Laughing aloud, Paris apologized for holding his brother up. This at least refocused Hector, whose thoughts still lingered with his wife and son, on the business at hand, and his perennial irritation with his wayward sibling softened. Recognizing the soldier inside the playboy, he confessed he was hurt when he overheard the men heaping their contempt on Paris. Now was his opportunity to redeem himself in their eyes, and so the brothers rode out to battle in the same chariot, closer perhaps, emotionally as well as physically, than at any point since the war began.

The Trojan hero – and antihero – made an immediate impact upon their return. Hector killed Eioneus, and Paris killed Menesthius. Inspired by their example, Glaucus killed Iphinous. Sensing the Achaean tide ebbing, Athena sought to intervene, but Apollo, Troy's staunchest ally, bade her back off. The Olympian rivals agreed to resolve their differences through a personal duel of proxies. Athena bade Helenus inform Hector of this plan, and the two immortals, adopting the morbid disguise of carrion birds, settled down to watch atop a broad towering oak.

Achilles rendered in all his glory as a statue presented by the women of England to the Duke of Wellington. The Achaean warlord's heroic proportions were cast, appropriately, from cannon taken in the Peninsular War and at Waterloo. (Maurice Savage / Alamy)

Hector issued his challenge, on the terms that the winner might despoil his victim of arms and armour but return the body so that it might be honoured with the appropriate rites. A hushed silence fell over the Achaean ranks, who were ashamed to refuse such a challenge, but afraid to take it up, until Menelaus finally volunteered. Aware he was no match for Hector, and that with his demise would go the entire Achaean rationale for continuing the struggle over Helen, nine other warlords came forward. When the lots were drawn, the task of upholding Achaean honour fell to Ajax. His immense tower shield consisted of seven leather bull hides with an eighth layer of hammered bronze to top it off. Hector's spear cast penetrated six of those hides but was stopped by the seventh. Ajax's throw in return punched right through the centre of the Trojan's shield, and Hector had to dodge quickly to avoid the point.

With battle raging outside the walls of Troy, Andromache brought her young son, Astyanax, to bid farewell to his father, Hector, at the Scaean Gate. But the boy recoiled at the sight of his own father, all bristling terror. His parents laughed; it would be one of the last tender moments they would share. *The Parting of Hector and Andromache* by Joseph Marie Wien. (Peter Horree / Alamy)

Both men having retrieved their spears, Ajax lunged, again punching through Hector's shield and this time grazing his neck. Hector snapped back with a rock, but Ajax caught it on his shield and hurled a far larger stone that buckled Hector's knees, knocking him to the ground. Both men drew their swords, but as dusk was falling, heralds from each side intervened before they could come to blows, inquiring if the duel should be suspended. Ajax deferred this decision to Hector, who thought it best if both men concede to the night. Though their private duel was over, the war wasn't going anywhere, and both men would lead their armies into battle upon the morrow. For now, at least, it was appropriate they stand down with honours even. As a token of respect, Hector gave Ajax his silver-studded sword, and Ajax in return offered his war-belt, glistening purple. Little could either man have guessed the evils that would befall them from this innocent and honourable exchange.

Trojan Ascendancy

That night, in the Trojan council chamber, Antenor urged that Helen and all her treasures be returned to Menelaus. Paris refused to surrender Helen, but as to the treasures he despoiled from Mycenae, he offered to return them and even contribute from his own hoard. But the Achaeans rejected this compromise offer, and the only concession Agamemnon would make was a truce to retrieve the dead.

When the battle was renewed the following morning, Zeus, in answer to the pleas of Thetis, launched his thunderbolts at the Achaeans, causing them to flee. Only Nestor stood firm, and he was brought down when Paris put an arrow into the brain of one of his horses. Diomedes had to scoop the aged veteran aboard his own chariot in his flight.

With the Achaeans in full retreat, Agamemnon could only beg the gods to stop the Trojans from mowing down his men and let them escape with their lives if nothing else. Zeus, dismayed at the sight of the high king's tears, sent a sign, an eagle, clutching a fawn in its talons. Inspired by this omen, the Achaeans rallied.

Teucer followed up behind the charge, lurking under the wall of giant Ajax's shield, which concealed him head to toe. As his half-brother raised the rim, the archer would mark a target, shoot through the lines, and duck back under cover. By this means, Teucer shot down Orsilochus, Ormenus, Ophelestes, Daetor, Chromius, Lycophontes, Amopaon, and Melanippus, but to his frustration he could not claim the biggest prize: "I still can't bring this mad dog Hector down!" It wasn't for lack of trying. With his next shot he took out Gorgythion, and then he struck Hector's driver Archeptolemus. Hector leapt down from the chariot, hit the earth with a yell, seized a rock, and went for Teucer. The archer had just notched another arrow and was about to let fly when Hector, helmet flashing, caught him in the chest between heart and throat with his improvised missile. Teucer dropped to one knee, dazed, as the bow slipped from his grasp.

The archer was borne from the field, covered by Ajax, and Hector pursued the long-haired Argives as they fled in panic to the stockade that defended their ships. Back through the stakes and across the trench they fled, and hordes were cut down at the Trojans' hands in the total rout. As the Achaeans manned the wall of their stockade they gazed out at Hector as he paced his chariot along the trench's edge, wheeling back and forth, his eyes glaring bright as a Gorgon's.

Hector, determined not to lose the momentum of the day, resolved to keep the army on the open plain. He dispatched heralds into the city to warn the boys too young and the men too old for fighting age to take up posts on the towers, and the women to keep the home fires burning, so no raiding parties could slip inside the walls while the army was camped on the battlefield.

(OVERLEAF)
The motives of those rallying to the defense of Troy were as diverse as the heterogeneous nature of the allied coalition she assembled. Some fought for honour and glory on the field of battle; some for gold; some out of filial obligation. For the Trojans themselves, the cause was simple. They took up arms to defend the things they loved: their city, their hearths and homes, their wives and children waiting and watching from the battlements.

LAOCOON

HECUBA

PRIAM

HECTOR

CASSANDRA

PARIS

MEMNON

ANDROMACHE

AENEAS

ASCANIUS

ASTYANAX

PENTHESILEA

An Embassy to Achilles

Behind the walls of their stockade, Agamemnon summoned his men. Their commander in chief, tears streaming down his face, blamed cruel Zeus for tricking him into coming to Troy. They would never take the city, Agamemnon declared. They should all return to their ships and sail for home.

This speech was greeted in stony silence. Finally, Diomedes rose and bluntly repudiated Agamemnon's defeatism. Zeus had bestowed on him greater honours than any man alive, Diomedes chided, but this was all wasted if he did not possess the courage to match. If the high king wanted to slink home, he was free to do so, but even if Agamemnon took the rest of the army with him, Diomedes pledged that he and his faithful Sthenelus would continue to fight on.

Nestor advised Agamemnon to reconcile with Achilles. The high king recognized the wisdom of this course, for the son of Thetis alone was worth an army. He admitted to being blinded by his own all-consuming rage, but now, at last, he was ready to make amends, even if it cost him a fortune to win back Achilles' favour. Accordingly, he was prepared to offer goods, gold, a dozen prime stallions, and seven slave women, flawless in their beauty and skilled in their crafts. With them would go Briseis. Agamemnon would also offer that

THE TROJAN FORCES

Troy could not hope to stand against the combined armies of all Achaea without help. But her wealth and status enabled her to weave together a patchwork coalition of neighbouring states, each of which contributed native contingents to her cause. Homer tells us that Troy had armies of allies, which spoke a thousand different languages.

Leading the Adrestians were Adrestus and Amphius, sons of King Merops of Percote, serving Troy in defiance of their father, who had refused to let his two boys march to this all-consuming war. Alongside them stood Acamas and Pirus, who led the Thracians with their waving topknots. Euphemus led the Ciconians, while the Pelasgian spearmen were led by the brothers, Hippothous and Pylaeus. Odius and Epistrophus brought the Halizonians. Pylaemenes, son of Melius, led the Paphlagonians. Antiphus and Mesthles brought the Maeonians. Chromius and Ennomus led the Mysians. The Paeonian archers were captained by Pyraechmes. The Carians with their wild and barbarous tongues came with Amphimacus and Nastes, who came to battle covered in gold jewellery. Finally, the Lycians came from far to the south led by Sarpedon and Glaucus.

The greatest of the allies was Aeneas, the son of Anchises and the goddess Aphrodite. He led his Dardanians to the aid of Troy after Achilles had despoiled his estates at Mt. Ida, driving off his cattle. But, although married to Priam's daughter Creusa, he remained ambiguous in his loyalty. He held back from the Trojan assault on the Achaean ships out of anger at Priam's neglect of his contribution to the Trojan cause.

The allies retained their independence, and Dictys of Crete refers to the fact that "their different customs and different languages caused them to fight in disorder and turmoil." Nor did their support come cheap. The Achaeans were committed to a victory that would bring them much plunder, but, ironically, Troy had already been pillaged by her own partners. For all her once-fabled wealth, Hector explained to his allies, she had been stripped of her treasures to bear the cost of the war. Thus it was the fate of the city to be looted by those fighting for her, as well as against her.

when Troy was taken Achilles would be free to claim as much of the city's gold and bronze as he desired, and the twenty Trojan women of his choice. In addition, upon his return home he could choose from among Agamemnon's three (surviving) daughters one as his bride, and with her a dowry of seven citadels from Agamemnon's own domain.

Odysseus, Phoenix, and Ajax were selected as Agamemnon's ambassadors. When this trio arrived at the Myrmidon ships they found Achilles playing on a lyre. Only Patroclus was with him. Achilles welcomed the delegation and together they sat down to a meal. After raising a toast to their host, Odysseus began by pointing out that with Hector triumphant the Achaean cause teetered on the brink of disaster. Unless Achilles intervened, he feared the gods

Again and again the whim of Zeus would tip the scales of battle, now in favour of the Achaeans, now of Troy. The arbiter of fighting men's fate, to prevent a clash between Diomedes and Hector, he cast a thunderbolt under the hoofs of Diomedes' team.

would allow Hector to consummate his victory, and the once-mighty Achaean host would be fated to die at Trojan hands. He pleaded for Achilles to let go of the hatred devouring his heart before it was too late. He listed the peace offerings of Agamemnon, adding that if these just made him despise the high king all the more, then he should remember the glory that would be his, if he could kill Hector.

Even this appeal to Achilles' ego and desire for glory was not enough. His mother had prophesied that if he joined the enterprise against Troy, he would meet his destiny there, but his glory would never die. If he sailed back to Phthia he would lose his place in history but would live a long life consummated by marriage and fulfilled by fatherhood. He now embraced the latter course. He would sail for home, and advised the rest of the army to do the same while they still could.

Even a mythical war has its downtime. With the goddess Athena as their spectator (or judge?), Achilles and Ajax play dice – the game invented by their erstwhile comrade, Palamedes. (The Art Archive / Alamy)

He informed Phoenix that Odysseus and Ajax would carry his refusal back to Agamemnon, but that the old man would stay the night. With that, he gave Patroclus a sharp glance, a quiet nod, to pile the bedding for Phoenix, a sign to the other ambassadors they should think about leaving.

But Ajax, too simple to get the hint or too dogged to take it, would not depart without a few blunt words of his own, fighting man to fighting man. He accused Achilles of selling out his comrades-in-arms, all for the sake of just one girl when here he was offered seven. Achilles was moved but offered little in terms of compromise. He bid the ambassadors return with the message that he would not intervene in the battle until Hector fought all the way to the Myrmidon ships – which, given they were at the far end of the Achaean beachhead, would be scant solace to Agamemnon.

Meanwhile, Agamemnon took charge of the wall at night, walking the perimeter and ordering its defence. In a bid to discern the enemy's intentions, he dispatched Diomedes and Odysseus on a night patrol. The two Achaeans waylaid a Trojan, Dolon, the only son of the scared Trojan herald Eumedes. After extracting information from him in exchange for a pledge to spare his life, they murdered Dolon in cold blood, and then used this intelligence windfall to infiltrate the Thracian camp on the far end of the Trojan line. There they slaughtered King Rhesus and twelve of his men as they slept and drove their horses back to the Achaean lines. Their exploits helped boost morale, but the true test would come the next day.

Hector at High Tide

At dawn, battle was resumed. This day was the aristeia of Agamemnon. In the absence of Achilles, and with his campaign in the balance, he had to step up, and he did. First he killed both Isus and Antiphus, two sons of Priam who shared a chariot. Then he struck down Pisander and combat-hardened Hippolochus.

In the frenzy of his battle fury, Agamemnon drove the Trojans back to the Scaean Gates. There he encountered Iphidamas, the rough and rangy son of Antenor, who had brought twelve ships to the aid of Troy. Agamemnon cast at him but missed; Iphidamas drove his spear into Agamemnon's belly but the point failed to penetrate his armour. Agamemnon seized the shaft, dragged Iphidamas within range of his sword, and hacked his neck open. Having stripped the body he had turned back to the Achaean lines with the armour when Iphidamas' brother Coon swooped in from his blindside and slashed open his forearm from elbow to wrist. The wound did not prevent Agamemnon from taking Coon's head off and continuing to lead the assault.

Hector led a counter-charge, killing Asaeus, Opheltius, Agelaus, Aesymnus, Orus, and Hipponous. The Achaeans were routing until Diomedes and Odysseus rallied them, killing the two sons of Merops, among others. When Hector charged this duo, Diomedes caught him in the head with a cast spear. Hector's helmet deflected the point but the blow left him stunned. Paris then pinned Diomedes' foot to the ground with an arrow. After it was extracted he had to be evacuated back to the ships.

That left Odysseus alone on the front line. He struck down one Trojan after another, but a shaft cast by his enemies punched through his hide shield and then found a gap in his breastplate, flaying the skin clean off his ribs. Crying out for aid, his pleas were answered by Menelaus and Ajax, bearing his great tower shield. Menelaus bore Odysseus back to his chariot.

Ajax then plunged into the fray, shattering ranks of spearmen in his onslaught. At the opposite end of the line, where the fighters fell in the greatest numbers and grim incessant war cries rose around tall Nestor and battle-hardened Idomeneus, Hector drove amidst them, spearing or riding down rank after rank of the enemy.

Cebriones pointed out to Hector where Ajax wrought ruin on the Trojan line, routing all before him and driving them pell-mell. They turned their chariot to where the action was hottest and sped the careering car into both milling armies, trampling shields and corpses, churning up torrents of blood. When the Achaeans swung about and locked their shields, Hector drove against them again and again, giving his spear no rest. As the Achaeans fell

back, Ajax alone held off the Trojan pursuit, wheeling on the foe eagerly snapping at his heels.

Hector's assault snapped to an abrupt halt at the trench. Polydamas advised against a frontal assault but suggested dismounting and proceeding on foot. This approach was wiser, Hector conceded, and so the Trojan forces were marshalled in five battalions, each assigned a sector of the wall. The first and greatest force, comprising the Trojan elite, was led by Hector, with Polydamas at his shoulder. Paris led the second, supported by Alcathous and Antenor's son Agenor. Helenus, his brother Deiphobus, and Asius, son of Hyrtacus, led the third. The fourth was led by Aeneas, flanked by Antenor's two sons, Acamas and Archelochus. Sarpedon led the fifth, with Glaucus and Asteropaeus his lieutenants. Since the Trojans were facing north, the left of their line was towards the west and the sunset. Their tactical dispositions completed, wedging tight, shield-to-shield, they rushed the Achaean defences, and desperate fighting erupted along the wall. As Zeus kicked up a dust storm into the faces of the defenders, Hector launched his battalion against the main gate in the centre.

The eastern city gate in the boundary walls of ancient Troy. Though its ruins today amount to little more than the faintest echo of the glory brought to life by Homer, this physical manifestation of his world endows the site with a mystique like nowhere else. (The Art Archive / Alamy)

Meanwhile, Sarpedon and Glaucus led the Lycians under their command swarming up against the breastwork. Menestheus, holding that sector of the wall, sent an urgent message seeking assistance; Ajax and Teucer came to his aid, the former crushing the skull of Epicles with a rock, the latter putting an arrow into the shoulder of Glaucus. But Sarpedon came on, driving a spear into Alcmaon and dragging him headfirst from the wall. Then Sarpedon, clawing at the battlements with his bare hands, wrenched so hard an entire section of the palisade came away, planks and all, leaving the rampart exposed. Neither Teucer's arrows nor Ajax's spear could drive the son of Zeus back as his Lycians rallied to him, and a dreadful struggle ensued for control of the breach.

At the centre of the Achaean line, Hector grabbed a boulder, blunt at the base but tapering to a jagged point, that no two men could ordinarily lift; but Zeus, determined to give him the glory of being first to storm the wall, endowed him with the strength to hoist it and hurl it against the gate. Under its impact the planking shattered in a flying storm of splinters. His eyes flashing fire, Hector burst through the ruined defences, a spear in each fist, and behind him rushed the warriors of Troy.

Battle for the Ships

His purpose satisfied, Zeus now lost interest in the outcome and turned his attention elsewhere. Sensing his brother's absence, Poseidon intervened, rallying the Achaeans to mass in a shield wall to meet the Trojan charge. Idomeneus spurred his men forward, striking down many Trojans, including Asius, who fell with a spear point driven in under his chin.

Two sons of Priam were wounded in the fray – Deiphobus, speared by Meriones in the shoulder, and Helenus, whose bow hand was struck through by Menelaus. Paris was still active with his arrows, however, and shot down Euchenor, son of the Prophet Polyidus. His father had told him he would meet his end either at Trojan hands or of a fatal plague at home, so Euchenor had sailed off to war, both to save his wealth from the heavy fine the Achaeans levied on draft-dodgers and to seek a more glorious death than from some wasting disease.

Hector smashed the Achaean lines at the spot where the wall dipped lowest to the ground, where the ship of long-lost Protesilaus still lay hauled up on the beach. Bulked up against the waves of Trojans descending upon them were Boeotians, Ionians in their long skirts of armour, Locrians, Phthians, and men of Epea, renowned warriors who fought to hold Hector; but nothing they did could thrust him off their lines.

It was the Locrian light-armed troops who tilted the balance. Loosing salvo on pelting salvo from their bows and slings of springy, twisted wool, they tore the Trojan battle lines to pieces. While the Achaean elite grappled with Hector at the front, the Locrians continued to rain missiles from the rear until the Trojan troops finally broke under the deluge of missiles descending upon them. With the Trojan centre on the brink of collapse, Polydamas urged Hector to withdraw. He found Paris, at last showing his mettle, rallying the Trojan left flank. Together, the brothers led fresh reserves into the thickest of the fighting.

Agamemnon lost his nerve. He ordered the ships readied for a general evacuation at nightfall. This time it was Odysseus who rounded on the high king with contempt, pointing out that the men under his command would never hold a defensive line if they saw the ships being hauled out to sea. They would break, and in the panic, the mad rush to scramble on board the nearest vessel, the entire Achaean host would be swept away.

Diomedes urged the other warlords, wounded as they were, to lead their battalions back into the fray. Meanwhile, Hera, though her heart was poisonous with loathing for her husband, nonetheless succeeded in beguiling and seducing Zeus. As he slumbered in post-coital bliss the Achaeans rallied. Ajax caught Hector with a rock, one of the countless holding-stones for the ships rolling at the fighters' feet. The blow sent the Trojan prince spinning like a top to the ground, and in his absence, the Achaeans thrust the Trojans back, Ajax cutting down Antenor's son Archelochus.

When Zeus awakened he immediately discerned Hera's intent and its implications. He first ordered Poseidon out of the fray. His brother, reluctantly, obeyed. Next, Apollo was dispatched to rouse Hector and lead the Trojan assault, bridging the trench and tearing down the wall with the same ease a boy at the seashore might kick over a sandcastle. Hector charged head-on at Ajax. While the two fought it out for the Achaean's ship, Hector's cousin Caletor sought to ignite it. Ajax stopped him short with a spear thrust to the chest. As he crumpled into the dust, the torch slipping from his fingers, Teucer aimed

Defying the order of his brother Zeus, Poseidon slipped into the Achaean camp in the guise of the seer Calchas to rally the defense of the ships. Singling out Ajax and Aias, he roused their hearts and bodies with the energy needed to hold the line against Hector's onrushing Trojans.

The tides of war rolled back and forth throughout the conflict. The lowest ebb for the Achaeans came when, in the absence of Achilles, they were driven back to their last line of defence, the very ships that had borne them to Troy. The entire campaign now hinged on the outcome of this confrontation. Urged on by Hector, the Trojans strained to unleash fire against the wooden hulls. Rallied by mighty Ajax and his long spear, the Achaeans fought with their backs to the broad sea to maintain their beachhead.

his next shaft at Hector, only for Zeus to snap the twisted cord on his bow just as the archer drew it taut against his man.

Hector, sensing the entire war now hung in the balance, threw himself against the Achaean shield wall until it finally broke, driving the routed foe back upon their ships. Ajax alone held the line. Up and down the decks of the ships he went with his great plunging strides, swinging his enormous polished pike, twenty-two forearms long. With the Trojans closing for the kill, Hector, at last, grappled a ship's stern, the vessel that had borne Protesilaus to Troy. Battle raged around that ship as Achaeans and Trojans hacked each other at close range. Hector held fast, clinging to the high stern, arms locked in a death grip, crying out for his men to bring fire.

Not even Ajax could hold his ground. Under the barrage of Trojan arrows descending upon him from all directions. He backed away by inches, then leapt down to the seven-foot bridge amidships. From there his huge pike kept beating the Trojans off the hulls, all the time bellowing out to the routed Achaeans to turn and fight. There was nowhere to run; it was stand or die. With each cry, he thrust his deadly pike with a fresh new fury, and any Trojan crashing against the beaked ships, torch ablaze in hand, would find Ajax ready and waiting there. Twelve men he impaled as they struggled up the hulls.

The Counterfeit Achilles

Patroclus, in tears, urged Achilles to intervene, or to at least send him into battle at the head of the Myrmidons, wearing Achilles' armour, so the Trojans, thinking Achilles had entered the fray, might give ground and allow the Achaeans some breathing room. With the fresh ranks of the Myrmidons in the van the Achaeans might yet roll the battle-weary enemy back to Troy.

By way of reply, Achilles started to reiterate all his grievances against Agamemnon, but in mid-tirade he suddenly broke off. "Enough. Let bygones be bygones. Done is done. How on earth can a man rage on forever?" But still his pride held him back; "I said I would not relax my anger, not till the cries and carnage reached my own ships." He therefore gave leave for Patroclus to serve in his stead, urging him to strike the Trojans with full force. However, he instructed Patroclus, once he had driven the enemy from the fleet he must not push his assault to the walls of Troy herself. Achilles feared both for the life of Patroclus and for his own renown. Should his proxy succeed in ending the war that day, to him would go the laurels of victory. While Achilles waxed rhapsodic in his fantasy, Ajax was at the end of his tether, his shield and helmet ringing with repeated blows, fighting for breath, gasping, bathed in the sweat pouring down his body, his limbs soaked and sleek. Seizing his chance, Hector lunged at the giant Achaean and took the head off his pike. Watching the bronze point bounding away, Ajax fell back. In his absence the Trojans flung torch upon torch against the vessel, and within moments the ship of Protesilaus was engulfed in flames.

Seeing the blaze go up, Achilles now urged Patroclus into battle, mustering his Myrmidons, fifty fighters from each of the fifty ships that sailed from Pythia to Troy. These were arranged into five battalions, headed by Menesthius, Eudorus, Pisander, the old horseman Phoenix, and Alcimedon. These men had chafed under the confinement their lord had imposed upon them, and Achilles was well aware of the muttered discontent directed towards him. Now, he informed them, they would be unleashed into the raging battle they had longed for.

Patroclus, too, weighed in, telling the Myrmidons they must win great honour for their warlord, so Agamemnon might regret disgracing the man he needed most to win his war. Achilles and Patroclus were of a similar mind, in that the most important thing in the world for both of them was Achilles.

Patroclus caught the Trojans, who were fixated on destroying the ships, off guard with his sudden, unlooked for assault. Among the first to fall was Pyraechmes, the firebrand who led the Paeonians, the master riders from Amydon, who broke and ran at the death of their chief. A general retreat of the Trojans ensued, as Patroclus drove them back from the ships, leaving Protesilaus' hulk half-burned but still upright. However, the main bulk of the Trojan army was not routed; they braced for battle and made a stand.

Mighty deeds were accomplished that day by fighters both renowned and unknown. Nestor's sons, Antilochus and Thrasymedes, slew Sarpedon's stalwart comrades Atymnius and Maris, the two sons of Amisodarus, he who bred the Chimaera. Idomeneus skewered Erymas straight through the mouth, driving his spearhead up under the brain to split the Trojan's glistening skull. Both nostrils spurting, mouth gaping, blowing convulsive sprays of blood and teeth, Erymas embraced death even as his corpse fell to the ground.

As soon as Patroclus cut the foremost battalions off, he pivoted to pin them against the warships and prevent them seeking the walls of Troy for safety. Pronous was the first to fall to his spear, then Thestor, cowering in his chariot, crazed with fear when Patroclus rose up alongside him and thrust into his jawbone, ramming the spearhead square between his teeth so hard he hooked him over the chariot-rail like an angler drawing some fish from the sea, flipping him face down on the Earth. Next he killed Erylaus at long range, catching him with a rock square between the eyes as he closed in. Then in a blur of kills, he took down Amphoterus, Erymas, Epaltes, Tlepolemus, Echius and Pyris, Ipheus and Euippus and Polymelus.

Sarpedon leapt from his chariot to engage Patroclus, much to the dismay of Zeus, who lamented the loss of the mortal he loved most, his own son, now doomed to die. He contemplated intervening, but Hera warned that if he cheated fate he would lose the respect of all Olympus.

Patroclus caught Sarpedon's driver, Thrasymelus, with the cast of his spear; Sarpedon hurled next and took down Patroclus' trace horse. As the creature convulsed, the paired horses of his team reared apart, sending the reins flying, fouled as the horse thrashed the dust in its death-throes, until Automedon leapt in with drawn sword and cut the dying beast free.

Achilles tends the wounds of Patroclus on this red-figured cup by the Sosias Painter, c. 500 BC. Such intimacy characterized their relationship. (Mary Evans / INTERFOTO / ARTCOLOR)

Again Sarpedon missed, but with his second throw Patroclus skewered the Lycian through the chest. Sarpedon's last words were for Glaucus, to take command of the Lycian contingent. Having lost their staunchest ally the Trojans crashed back into the Achaeans as they sought to despoil Sarpedon's body. The Myrmidon Epigeus had just grasped the corpse when Hector smashed his head with a rock, his entire skull splitting apart. Patroclus gained revenge in like fashion on Sthenelaus and the battle intensified, with the body of the fallen Sarpedon its epicentre, buried under a mass of weapons, blood and dust, still attracting fighting men like flies to rich cream.

Finally, the Trojans broke, streaming back towards the city gates. Still Patroclus in his aristeia hounded their broken ranks, and body after body fell to the ground, cleaved by his sword or spear.

Patroclus Stands Alone

The only thing standing between Patroclus and total victory was Apollo. Three times the god beat him back from the city walls. At Patroclus' fourth charge Apollo, swelling in wrath and majesty, warned him that Troy was not fated to fall under his spear, for not even Achilles would be granted that signal honour. As Patroclus gave ground, Apollo sought out Hector, who had reined in at the Scaean Gate and was debating whether to rally his men once more on the open plain or withdraw to the ramparts. The god incited him to charge against Patroclus, scattering Argives to each side as he drove. Patroclus accepted the challenge, smashing in the face of Hector's driver, Cebriones, with one throw of a jagged rock. Hector sprang down from his chariot and the two fought over the corpse like beasts of prey over fresh-killed game. Hector seized the head, Patroclus the feet, and as their tug-of-war ensued other fighters were drawn in, Trojans, Argives, all in a gruelling, maiming melee.

At last, the Achaeans broke through. As they stripped their trophy, Patroclus sought out the enemy, fired for the kill. Three times he charged, screaming his savage war cry, and three times he killed nine men. At the fourth charge, Apollo had finally had enough. The god struck the helmet from Patroclus' head, and under his horses' hoofs it tumbled, clattering on with its four forged horns and its hollow blank eyes until its plumes were all smeared in the bloody dust. Still Apollo struck, again and again. Patroclus' spear was shattered, his shield was stripped from his arm, his breastplate wrenched off. Dazed, exposed, vulnerable, Patroclus was impaled by Euphorbus, a novice but already the best of his age with the spear. The lifeblood draining from his body, Patroclus was weaving back to the Achaean lines when Hector struck and rammed his spear home, stabbing deep in the bowels, the point jutting straight out through Patroclus' back. He planted a heel against Patroclus' chest, wrenched his brazen spear from the wound, and kicked him over, flat on his back, free and clear of the weapon.

With Hector trying in vain to corral Achilles' horses and chariot, Menelaus strode up and took a stand over the corpse of Patroclus, spearing Euphorbus through the throat when he tried to claim his prize. When Hector rounded on him, Menelaus chose discretion as the better part of valour and gave ground, seeking for Ajax. Hector succeeded in stripping off Achilles' armour, flinging the burnished gear to his waiting troops to haul away to Troy. But Glaucus abruptly intruded on his moment of triumph, insisting he return to the field to recover the body of Patroclus as ransom for that of Sarpedon. Otherwise, he would pull every single Lycian out of the line and march for home, Troy be damned.

Hector wasn't in the mood for this kind of lecture, not from a Lycian, even a relatively intelligent one he had previously harboured a certain respect for. But, aware that he could not realistically continue the war effort without the support of his allies, Hector exchanged his armour for that of Achilles and led his combined forces back into the fray.

The Body of Patroclus

Even great Ajax paused at the sight of the Trojan onslaught, losing hope that he and Menelaus could fight their way out, never mind securing the corpse of Patrolcus. All the mighty son of Telamon could see was the Trojan horde rolling towards him like a stormcloud, and at its head Hector, rushing at them headlong like death incarnate. At the last moment Achaean reinforcements led by Aias and Idomeneus arrived, just in time to meet the Trojan onslaught, crashing against their hastily-formed lines as heavy surf roars in against the rip at a river's mouth.

Hippothous lashed a shield-strap around Patroclus' ankles and was hauling him through the melee when Ajax stepped in and drove his spear right into Hippothous' helmet. His brains promptly burst from the wound in sprays of blood, soaking the weapon's socket. When Phorcys stepped up Ajax eviscerated him. Hector in return struck down Schedius, the point of his spear splitting the collarbone, stabbing through the body and out between the shoulder blades. The Argives finally locked together into a tight circle, ringing Patroclus round on all sides, spears jutting, shoulder-to-shoulder as Ajax bellowed out commands, ordering that no-one take a step back, nor break ranks to seek the glory of single combat.

The Trojans clawed desperately at this shield wall, and the earth ran red with blood, slithering dark now with the soldier's corpses tumbling thick and fast. The men who fought at long range could break off, but those holding the centre suffered agonies trapped as they were in the haze and carnage, the pitiless bronze hacking their lines to pieces, there where the bravest fought.

Achilles, watching the battle with mounting foreboding, had his worst fears realized when fleet-footed Antilochus, weeping, broke the news that Patroclus had fallen. Achilles collapsed, totally consumed with grief. Both hands clawing the ground for soot and filth, he poured it over his head, fouling his beautiful face, tearing at his hair, while Antilochus knelt alongside him, clutching his hands for fear he would turn his sword against his own flesh.

Such was her son's agony that Thetis came from the ocean's depths to comfort Achilles, cradling his head. "I've lost the will to live," her son

This funerary mask, beaten from a single sheet of gold, was discovered in 1876 by Heinrich Schliemann during his excavations at Mycenae. It was immediately dubbed the 'Mask of Agamemnon' but in fact predates the accepted period of the Trojan War by more than three centuries. (The Art Archive / Alamy)

told her, "unless, before all else, Hector is battered down by my spear and gasps away his life, the blood-price for Patroclus."

"You're doomed to a short life, my son," Thetis replied, "For hard on the heels of Hector's death your death must come at once –"

"Then let me die at once!" Achilles resolved. As for his feud with Agamemnon, "Enough. Let bygones be bygones. Done is done. Despite my anguish, I will beat it down, the fury mounting inside me, down by force. But now I'll go and meet that murderer head-on, that Hector who destroyed the dearest life I know."

Meanwhile, the battle for Patroclus' body raged on. Three times Hector seized his feet, wild to drag him off. Three times Ajax and Aias drove him back. Hector would have prevailed had Hera not dispatched Iris with a message to Achilles. Although bereft of armour, his mere presence as he stood at the trench, uttering his war cry, a blazing light sent by Athena illuminating the battlefield, was enough to panic the Trojan ranks, inducing them to withdraw and enabling the Achaeans to at last bear Patroclus' lifeless form to their camp.

Polydamus, who shared a birthday with Hector, urged the Trojan prince to fall back to the city. With Achilles back in the fight, it would be inviting disaster to meet him on the open plain, he reasoned. But Hector was stubborn. He would not concede the initiative; at daybreak he would launch another full-scale assault on the Achaean ships.

All night the Achaeans mourned Patroclus, Achilles leading the dirge. Meanwhile, Thetis had ascended to Olympus, to plead for Hephaestus to work new armour worthy of her son. With his matchless skill the god of the forge presented her with a helmet, breastplate, greaves, and shield, all imbued with a terrible beauty.

The next morning Achilles prowled along the water's edge, crying his piercing cry and summoning the Achaean warriors. Even those who'd kept to the

This statue, from the Loggia dei Lanzi in Florence, celebrates the *aristeia* (finest moment) of Menelaus. Up until then very much the junior partner of the Atrides family, when Agamemnon's brother witnessed Patroclus being cut down by Hector it was he who stood astride the body, rescuing it from Trojan desecration. (Glenn Harper / Alamy)

beached ships till now, from the helmsmen to the stewards left on board to assign rations, trooped to the muster.

Many were wounded, including Diomedes and Odysseus, who limped in late. Last to arrive was Agamemnon. Achilles immediately addressed him, asking whether their mutual rage, all for the sake of a slave girl, had accomplished anything. Because of this petty feud, how many comrades had fallen, he reflected, brought down by the enemy while he sat nursing his rage in bitter isolation. Now, he cast aside the anger consuming his heart.

As the mustered army roared its enthusiasm, Agamemnon, once again displaying his unique propensity for lowering himself to the occasion, responded with a rambling non-apology for the crisis that had brought his endeavour to the brink of ruin. Too proud to address Achilles by name, he continued to insist that he was not to blame for their falling out, that Zeus and Fate and the Furies had driven him to madness. Forced to accept reality because Hector was running rampant on the battlefield, he was now only too willing to fork over the treasures – including Briseis – he had promised earlier with his embassy. These tokens were now meaningless to Achilles. Having sworn off food and drink till Patroclus be avenged, he was willing to lead the Achaean ranks into battle then and there, famished as they were, for his only desires were slaughter, blood, and revenge. But Odysseus prevailed upon him to give the rank and file time and space to break their fast while he ritualistically donned the magnificent armour prepared for him by the gods. Later, In full

In this scene depicted on a 2nd century BC Etruscan urn, Menelaus and Meriones lift Patroclus' corpse onto a cart while Odysseus (on the right, wearing the pilos hat and bearing a shield) looks on. The death of Patroclus sorely tried the entire Achaean host, not just Achilles; around his corpse, Homer relates, all his loving comrades mourned. (PD)

battle array he mounted his chariot, an emissary of death, resplendent in glittering gold, silver and bronze, thirsting for his aristeia. Unleashing his war cry he lashed his team forward, the vast host at his heels slowly uncoiling and then, faster now, inundating the plain behind him.

The Aristeia of Achilles

As the Achaean and Trojan lines closed, all Olympus broke loose, the gods first rousing the rival armies to deeds of valour, then turning their pent-up jealousies on each other. Even as Zeus cast thunder, Athena and Ares clashed, and the earth quaked under Poseidon's lash. Achilles hunted for Hector. Encountering Aeneas, he mocked Troy's ally for his ambition, asking if he fought alongside his "stallion-breaking friends" in hopes of someday inheriting Priam's throne. If so, he was snared in a delusion of his own contrivance. "Even if you killed me, would Priam drop his crown in your hands – for that?" After an exchange of spears Achilles closed with his sword, only to find his foe had vanished. So the deathless gods loved Aeneas too, Achilles mused. The rest of his enemies were not so lucky. Iphition, Hippodamas, and Demoleon, a son of Antenor,

Athena and Apollo intervening in the fight between Hector and Achilles.

were the first casualties of his rage. His next victim was Polydorus, the youngest son of Priam, fleet of foot but forbidden by his father to fight. For all his speed, Achilles caught him in the square of his back as he dashed past.

Listening to his brother's shrill screams, watching him clutch his entrails as he died, the enraged Hector hurled his spear with all his might at Achilles. Athena blew it back, and it fell, impotent, at Hector's feet. Loosing savage war cries Achilles closed on Hector, but Apollo spirited the Trojan to safety, leaving Achilles swinging at the mist that shrouded him.

Now the slaughter began. Achilles cut down Dryops, smashed Demuchus' knee with a well-flung spear then sprang in to rip his life away with his sword. He butchered the brothers Laogonus and Dardanus as well as Tros, Mulius and Echeclus the son of Agenor. Then he transfixed Deucalion with his spear, before decapitating him with his sword. Frenzied, inhuman in his rage, Achilles rampaged on, merciless, unstoppable.

Once he reached the ford over the Scamander, Achilles split the routed Trojans, driving one half back towards the city, scattering across the plain. The other half tumbled, flailing, into the river. Achilles waded in after them, slaughtering until his arm grew weary. Only one man dared meet him face to face, the ambidextrous Asteropaeus, wielding two spears. He cast both simultaneously at the onrushing Achaean. Achilles caught the first in his shield, but the second grazed his right arm, drawing blood. Achilles hurled his spear in response, a miss, but with such force it plunged half its length into the riverbank. Asteropaeus tried desperately to wrench it free, then break it, but before he could do either, Achilles cut him down.

On Achilles sped, in a blur of death striking down Thersilochus, Mydon, Astypylus, Mnesus, Thrasius, Aenius and Ophelestes. Such was the carnage that the river itself, boiling over with horror, begged Apollo to stand by the Trojans and save whoever was left alive. When he heard that, Achilles leapt down from the bluff and plunged into the river's heart. Blinded by his rage, he had picked a fight even he couldn't win. Scamander rose up against him, churning, surging, all his rapids rising in white fury into a tremendous wave. Recoiling against its force, Achilles flung out his arms and clutched for an elm tree, but it was torn out by the roots, ripping away the entire bank. Down it crashed in a tangled snarl of branches, temporarily damming the river. Bursting clear of the water, Achilles dashed for the plain, but Scamander would not let him go, looming into a murderous breaker, ominously dark, behind him. Achilles could not outrun the river, and when he turned to stand and fight it crashed down upon him, tugging at his knees with its current, striving to drag him under. Drenched, drowning, buffeted by the swirling corpses of the very men he had laid low, Achilles despaired. Better Hector had struck him down, better to die a hero's death at the hands of the greatest warrior in the Trojan ranks, than to die like this.

But the gods heard his pleas. Hephaestus unleashed the flames from his forge, and Hera drove the winds to fan them. Caught in the inferno, Scamander writhed and boiled, begged the Olympians to let him be. Releasing Achilles, the river returned to his banks, and the son of Thetis returned to his killing.

The Fate of Hector

Watching from the battlements his army in full flight, Priam ordered the gates flung open to give as many of the routed Trojans as possible a chance to regain the safety of the city. In headlong flight they came, streaming into Troy, any fighter whose racing legs could save his life. To give them more time, Apollo took the form of Agenor and led Achilles in a chase across the plain. In his wake, the Achaeans closed up to the walls of Troy. Of all her defenders, only Hector still held his ground at the Scaean Gates. Apollo cut short his diversion of Achilles, who, enraged by this deception, pounded remorselessly towards the city.

Priam was the first to see him coming, surging over the plain. He moaned in despair, lamenting that this man, who had already robbed him of so many sons, was now descending upon his beloved heir. "Don't just stand there, don't, dear child," he implored Hector; "Back, come back! Inside the walls, my boy!" In that moment he foresaw the fate of the city, its doom inextricably linked with that of Hector, laid low and despoiled. Hecuba, too, begged her firstborn son to seek shelter. The king and queen of Troy, wailing and pleading on the battlements, could not shake Hector's resolve, but as he waited he had time to turn over his options in his mind. There was no way out, he concluded. If he withdrew inside the city he would cede authority to Polydamas, who had counselled retiring the army behind the walls. And how much better it would have been had he heeded that advice, Hector had to admit. His own reckless pride had led the flower of Troy to its ruin. So now he would redeem himself or die in the attempt, kill Achilles or fall at his hands, return to the city in triumph or return to the Earth from whence all men come.

But when he saw Achilles racing towards him, the bronze around his body flaring like a raging fire or the rising sun, his resolve failed. Taking to his heels, he fled, Achilles in hot pursuit. Three times they circled the walls of Troy before Athena finally intervened. Taking the form of Deiphobus, she materialized at Hector's side, pledging to fight shoulder to shoulder.

Snarling "kill or be killed," Hector rounded on Achilles. He offered one final pledge, that whoever emerged the victor of their confrontation would

This 2nd century AD marble sarcophagus is bordered by a frieze depicting Priam's embassy to beg for the body of Hector. Kneeling down before Achilles, the King clasped his knees and kissed his hands, those warrior's hands that had slaughtered so many of his sons in battle. (The Art Archive / Alamy)

honour the body of whoever fell. But Achilles was in no mood to bargain; "don't talk to me of pacts," he shot back. "There are no binding oaths between men and lions – wolves and lambs can enjoy no meeting of the minds – they are all bent on hating each other to the death. So with you and me." With that, Achilles hurled his spear. Hector ducked under its flight, watching the bronze tip hurtle past and stab into the earth. But he never saw Athena retrieve it for Achilles. His own return throw struck his foe's shield dead centre only to glance away. He called to Deiphobus for another spear, but his brother was nowhere to be seen. At that moment, he realized his destiny had brought him to this moment, this place, and his time had come

Drawing his sword he launched himself at Achilles. But the son of Thetis knew the armour, his own armour, that Hector wore, knew its exposed spot, at the open throat. There he stabbed with his spear, bringing the prince of Troy crashing down. Still his rage was not yet sated. Not only did he gloat in his victory, he stripped the dying Hector of any dignity, any glory, pledging the dogs and birds would defile and disgrace his corpse. Hector begged only that his body be returned to his people to receive the last rites. But there was no mercy in Achilles, whose wrath blinded him to all kindness. Even as Hector prophesied Achilles' own death before the Scaean Gates, Achilles ripped his spear free. Troy's greatest warrior and most noble prince had fallen.

More and more Achaeans crowded closer to the body of Hector. They drove their blades into his corpse, laughing and gloating at how much easier he was to handle now than when he had hounded them back to the prows of their ships.

Grim Achilles took Hector's belt – the belt given him by Ajax – and, piercing the tendons, drove it through Hector's ankles. The he lashed them to his chariot and dragged the body behind him back to the ships.

To the victor the spoils; Achilles lashes the fallen Hector to his chariot and drags his body in triumph back to the Achaean ships. His comrades in arms trail joyously in his wake; the citizens of Troy watch on in horror from the battlements. Painting by Franz Matsch.

Hector's father and mother, watching from the battlements, gave vent to their unspeakable grief, and wailing seized the city. His wife was the last to know of Hector's fate. Weaving at her loom, setting the cauldron over the fire so her husband could enjoy his steaming hot bath when he came home from the battle, Andromache heard Hecuba's anguished cry, and foreboding struck her to the core. Her world, and that of their son, had changed forever. Words like marriage, and father, would hold no meaning for them now. Widow and orphan was their lot.

While the Trojans lamented, the Achaeans prepared sacrifices of their own for the funeral of Patroclus. Achilles honoured his pyre by offering honey and oil and piling up the bodies of sheep, cattle, dogs, horses, and prisoners of war. A dozen brave sons of the proud Trojans he hacked to pieces. The Achaeans held games in honour of Patroclus, and made merry in their sport, but still Achilles could not let go of the hatred that consumed him. Dawn found him wandering the shore, pacing alone. Then he lashed the corpse of Hector to his chariot, dragging it three times around Patroclus' tomb, and leaving it face down in the dust.

Twelve days had passed before the king of the gods decreed that Achilles must return the body of Hector. Thetis told her son of Zeus's command. Priam came in person at the head of his embassy, bearing rich gifts. Hermes led him safely through the Achaean lines, drugging the sentries with the sweet wine of sleep.

Achilles had just finished dinner when, to his astonishment, Priam appeared in his quarters. The old king knelt down and clasped Achilles' knees to beg him for the body of Hector. He offered a glittering ransom, invoking the gods and the memory of Achilles' own father. Both men wept. Then they broke bread together and soon arrived at terms for the return of Hector's body and a twelve day truce for the funeral rites and proper period of mourning.

At the end of his final journey, to the halls of the palace, Hector was serenaded with the laments of Trojan women. Hecuba and Helen mourned his death, while Andromache led their songs of sorrow, cradling her husband's head to her breast one last time. His body was cremated, the flames doused with glistening wine, and the ashes interred in a barrow overlooking the city he had given his life to defend. And so the Trojans buried Hector, breaker of horses.

THE WIDER WAR

Penthesilea, Queen of the Amazons

The death of Hector, their mightiest champion, left the Trojans numb with grief and foreboding, Priam in particular. Unwilling to take the field, they surrendered the initiative entirely to the Achaeans, who were now free to commence their assault against the city walls.

But from this low ebb, Trojan fortunes suddenly revived as aid arrived from foreign quarters. In this post-Homeric phase, the war evolved from a regional conflict between city states to a Greek struggle against the wider world, anticipating the encounters of subsequent generations with the great empires beyond the Aegean Sea.

The first of her exotic allies to arrive at Troy was Penthesilea, queen of the fabled Amazons, the race of warrior women. In quasi-exile after the accidental death of her sister, Hippolyta, in a hunting incident, Penthesilea brought only her twelve handmaids to Troy, named by Quintus Smyrnaeus: Clonie, Polemusa, Derinoe, Evandre, Antandre, Bremusa, Hippothoe, "dark-eyed Harmothoe," Alcibie, Derimacheia, Antibrote, and "Thermodosa glorying with the spear." Each of these was a warrior princess in her own right, but Penthesilea, as daughter of the war god Ares, outshone them all, a unique hybrid of "unearthly grace with battle-prowess clad."

Although few in number, the arrival of the Amazons rallied the Trojans, and the following morning, like a sudden blast of flame, Penthesilea led the Trojans into battle, catching the Achaeans, who did not anticipate such spirit in the absence of Hector, off guard.

In the first rush of her onslaught, Penthesileia cut down no fewer than eight Achaean champions. At her side the Amazon handmaids exacted their own toll. Laogonus was laid low by Derinoe, and Menippus by Clonie. Incensed, Podarces transfixed Clonie with his spear. Wheeling on him, Penthesileia drove a javelin through his right arm. Podarces withdrew from the battle only to subsequently bleed out and expire from his wound.

Now the Achaeans rallied. Idomeneus brought down Bremusa. Meriones killed Evandre and Thermodosa, one with a spear to the heart, the other with a lightning sword-thrust between the hips. Aias struck Derinoe between throat and shoulder with his spear, while Diomedes took the heads off Alcibie and Derimacheia.

Even as her handmaids fell about her, Penthesilea, screaming curses, surged on, wild as a tigress. She crashed through rank upon rank of the Achaeans, lashing out with javelin, battle-axe and her bow, which sent death winging into the breasts of those who defied her and the backs of those who fled from her.

Watching from the battlements as the contest raged below them were the women of Troy. One of their number, Tisiphone, seized with the passion of the moment, urged her peers to join the fight. According to Quintus Smyrnaeus, she insisted women "be not creatures cast in diverse mould from men: to us is given such energy of life as stirs in them," a fact vividly underscored by the prowess of Penthesilea, who fought on their behalf and not for her own country, home and family.

This fervour rippled through the women of Troy. They flung aside their weaving and picked up weapons, ready to rush out into the fray. Before they made it, Theano, the priestess of Apollo, intervened, reminding them they were unfit and unschooled for war, sharing nothing with Penthesilia, an Amazon trained to fight since birth, save her sex. She commanded the women to return to their looms and leave the fighting to men.

Achilles' slumber is disturbed by the shade of Patroclus, who warns that he, too, is fated to die in battle beneath the walls of Troy. The shade urges the two of them be as inseparable in death as they were in life, their bones being interred in the same two-handled gold urn that was a gift from Thetis. An 18th Century painting by Jacques Gamelin. (The Art Archive / Alamy)

AMAZONS – FACT OR FICTION?

In the *Iliad*, Priam refers to fighting alongside the Phrygians against the Amazons, describing them as *Antianeirai*, "a match for men in war." Herodotus labeled them *Androktones*, "killers of men", and maintained, "No girl shall wed till she has killed a man in battle." Emphasizing her alien nature, at a time when the Achaean and Trojan champions rode into battle on chariots and dismounted to slug it out on foot with sword and spear, Penthesilea is distinctive for being the only warlord throughout the saga to fight on horseback.

According to the dramatist Aeschylus, the motherland of the Amazons, "the maidens fearless in fight," was Scythia (modern day Ukraine) on the northern shore of the Black Sea. The first part of this narrative is supported by the archeological record. The Scythian-Sarmatian nomads, who dominated the Eurasian steppe in Classical antiquity, appear to have had – by comparison with their "civilized" neighbors – a remarkably egalitarian social structure. Evidence of high-ranking warrior women has emerged from excavations of Scythian burials in southern Ukraine and Russia. Approximately a fifth of Scythian-Sarmatian kurgans (ceremonial wooden chamber-tombs) on the lower Don and lower Volga Rivers contained females dressed for battle, usually including bows. The kurgan of the Pazyryk Scythian "Ice Maiden" contained no fewer than six horses. There is thus much to substantiate Pindar's description of "well-horsed Amazons… strong in their brazen bows."

Meanwhile, the Achaeans had been driven back to their ships. The Trojan/Amazon alliance had been able to seize the initiative because Achilles and Ajax were mourning at the graveside of Patroclus. Finally alerted to the impending catastrophe of their cause, the two warlords raced to where the fighting was fiercest. Their impact was immediate. Achilles cut a swathe through the remaining Amazons, striking down Antandre, Polemusa, Antibrote, fierce-souled Hippothoe, and Harmothoe.

Penthesilea hurled two javelins at Ajax. The first glanced off his shield, her second off his greaves. Ajax left the Amazon queen to Achilles, who transfixed her with one spear thrown at a distance and pinned her to her horse with another at close range. The Trojans, seeing their ally struck down, fled for the gates of their city.

As Achilles stood over his vanquished rival, the red rage drained from his eyes, and he was filled with remorse to have taken such beauty from the world, a warrior queen he might otherwise have borne home, the ideal consort for the warrior king of Phthia.

This wistful regret only provoked the contempt of Thersites, who mocked the mournful Achilles for losing sight of the warrior's path whenever his eyes lighted on a pretty face. Enraged, Achilles struck Thersites with such force his soul was ejected from his body even as all of his teeth were smashed from his mouth. The death of this jester was shrugged off by the Achaean host generally, exasperated as they were with his ridicule. The exception was Diomedes, kinsman to Thersites. He and Achilles nearly came to blows before cooler heads prevailed. The body of Penthesilea was delivered up to Priam, who had it cremated. Her ashes were interred in a place of honour next to those of a long dead Trojan king.

(OVERLEAF)
To the succor of Troy from a land far away, Penthesilea led her Amazons into the fray. With her engagement, the saga erupted in a clash of civilizations. Everything about her was alien and exotic to the Achaeans, clustered as they were in their Aegean cul-de-sac. A woman in a man's world, riding a horse into battle, clad in outlandish gear and crying out in a strange tongue, she was beauty and terror, blazing passion and icy resolve.

Memnon, King of the Ethiopians

With the death of Penthesilea, despair once again covered Troy. Speaking for many, Polydamus urged that Helen be returned to Menelaus, sparking a heated confrontation with Paris. Although not willing to surrender Helen, Priam still conceded the plain to the Achaeans, ordering his forces to remain on the defensive behind the battlements.

Then another ally arrived, stormy hearted Memnon, leading to Troy a numberless host of Ethiopia's warrior elite. The son of Tithonus and Eos, goddess of the dawn, he was received with great rejoicing in the beleagured city. But the honours bestowed made little impression on his contemplative character and martial professionalism. Declining to partake of the revels, he responded to the toasts in his name by quietly asserting that his success or failure in battle would prove his true worthiness.

The following morning, Memnon put those qualities to the test, leading the combined Trojan and Ethiopian force out to war. Achilles had not lost any of his edge, sending first Thalius, then Mentes, then many more Trojans besides crashing down into the dust. But for all the veteran fighters on the field, their skills honed by a decade of war, it was the Ethiopians who now ruled the blood-soaked fields of Ilium. At their head was Memnon, who cut down two renowned fighters, Pheron and Ereuthus.

Antilochus, striding forth to meet him, hurled his spear at Memnon. The King successfully swerved to avoid the missile, and leaped at Nestor's son, who countered by catching his opponent in the head with a stone. Memnon's helmet, however, took most of the force of the blow and, his ears ringing, the king transfixed Antilochus with his spear.

The anguished Nestor called on his surviving son, Thrasymedes, and a retainer, fiery-hearted Phereus, to retrieve Antilochus' corpse, even as Memnon stripped the armour from it. These two struck deep into the Ethiopian ranks, but could not reach their king. In his desperation, Nestor would have contested the issue himself had Memnon, for pity's sake, urged him not to throw away his remaining years so fruitlessly. Nestor perceived the wisdom of these words and fell back, lamenting the two had not met

Achilles contemplates the beauty of the fallen Penthesilea. The battle fury surging through him as he struck her down, he damned her to the dogs and ravens. But when he stripped back her helmet, his heart was broken with a pain he hadn't felt since the death of his beloved Patroclus. Illustration by H. J. Ford.

on equal terms, when he was in the full bloom of youth and could match spear for spear.

As Memnon drove his men on, Nestor sought out Achilles, who broke off from the Trojans in order to focus on this new threat. Memnon snatched up a huge rock, a boundary marker, from the field, and hurled it at the onrushing Achaean hero, but Achilles deflected it with his shield and then caught Memnon in the shoulder with a spear thrust. The king, however, not only took the blow but lunged forward and slashed Achilles across the arm.

What followed was the longest set-piece duel of the entire saga. The two men were so absolutely distinct – the dark Memnon and the fair Achilles – and yet so entirely similar: both kings, both the sons of goddesses, both wearing armour forged by Hephaestus. Even as the battle raged all around them, Memnon and Achilles continued to exchange blow for blow until finally Achilles' sword struck home, his dark-blue blade passing clean through the body of his royal foe.

Achilles at the Scaean Gates

Now the tide turned, as Achilles drove the Trojans and their demoralized allies to the Scaean Gates, scornfully ignoring the warning of Apollo to proceed no further. But the hour of his doom had arrived, as Paris sent an envenomed arrow winging into his ankle, into the tendon that would forever after bear his name. In agony, Achilles drew out the shaft, but already he could sense that the wound was mortal.

The Trojans rushed in, seeking to end his menace once and for all. But the rage still pulsed deep within Achilles. His spear lashed out to cut down many more of his foes, even as they turned and fled. But finally, his dauntless heart and mighty limbs overcome, the greatest of the Achaean warriors fell.

Still, Ajax stood his ground, and with his lance he thrust them all back from the body of Achilles. Any Trojan who ventured too near paid the price,

ACHILLES HEEL

Many retellings of the Trojan War maintain that Achilles was invulnerable to mortal harm save for the tendon that now bears his name. According to Apollonius, this was owed to his mother, Thetis, who "encompassed the child's mortal flesh in the night with the flame of fire; and day by day she anointed with ambrosia his tender frame, so that he might become immortal." However, his father, Peleus, interrupted this ritual before it was complete, so that his heel remained vulnerable. In the account of Statius, Thetis bathed her infant son in the River Styx, the boundary of the underworld, to "make his fair limbs impenetrable." Because she was holding him by the ankle when he was immersed in its waters, that tendon was never exposed to their magic. But these are later additions to the original myth. The claim that Achilles is invulnerable never appears in Homer. In fact, it contradicts the plot (why would an invulnerable man be so invested in a new suit of armour?) and events (Homer specifically refers to Achilles being wounded in battle).

including Glaucus, Troy's loyal ally to the end. Paris took aim at Ajax, but he, alert to the threat, struck the Trojan prince down with a stone. As Ajax hoisted Achilles' body clear of the fight he was covered by Odysseus, who took a fearsome toll on the Trojans even after one of them succeeded in driving a spear in behind his right knee.

Both sides broke off to mourn the honoured dead. Grieving for their king, the Ethiopians bore his body from the battlefield, withdrawing from the war. The Achaeans in turn lamented the loss of the man who had been their symbol and instrument of victory, and for many days they wept, Agamemnon among them.

The funeral of Achilles eclipsed even that of Patroclus. All around his pyre the Achaeans piled arms and armour, gold and amber, the corpses of sheep, cattle, horses, and prisoners of war. The Myrmidons cut off their hair and used it to shroud the body of their king. Briseis laid her own shorn tresses on

This 5th century BC *lekythos* (oil flask) depicts the dispute over the arms and armour of Achilles turning violent. Ajax has to be restrained from attacking Odysseus. His rage would ultimately consume him and drive him on to self-destruction. (The Art Archive / Alamy)

the corpse, as the torch was put to wood soaked by amphorae of oil, wine and honey, incense and sweet scented perfume.

The immolation and internment of Achilles' body left the question of who would receive his matchless armour. Ajax and Odysseus both staked their claim. Ajax insisted the judges be Idomeneus, Nestor, and Agamemnon, and Odysseus agreed. Nestor, however, pointed out that whoever the victor of their judgment, the loser would begrudge his success and the Achaean war effort would be the ultimate loser. He proposed referring the decision to the remaining Trojan captives.

As each man pled his case, Ajax, was overwhelmed by bitterness at Odysseus for even contesting the issue. He scorned his rival, labeling him a coward whose wits and treachery were his only true weapons.

On these grounds the Trojans pronounced Odysseus the victor, not a choice that reflected the will of the Achaean rank and file, from whom broke one deep groan when the result was announced.

Ajax's shock at the outcome consumed his mind. Refusing food or drink, unable to sleep, that night madness overcame him. In his rage he donned his armour and, clutching his sword, marched out to set the ships aflame and slaughter his erstwhile comrades, above all the guileful Odysseus, who had cheated him of his rightful prize. Thinking himself surrounded by Achaean warriors, he cut them all down, one by one. At first light his senses cleared and he beheld the plain all strewn with corpses – not of men, but of the sheep kept penned to be butchered for their meat. The shame of it was unendurable. In his last words laying a curse on Odysseus, Ajax fell on his sword – the sword given him by Hector – and died.

THE FALL OF TROY

The Next Generation: Eurypylus and Neoptolemus

So the Achaeans again assembled around the funeral pyre of a fallen champion. If Achilles had been the spearhead of their cause, so Ajax had been its shield.

Menelaus couldn't accept any more comrades falling because of him and Helen. He urged them all to abandon the war, before any more were killed. Calchas, the seer, agreed that the Achaean cause was hopeless unless the son of Achilles stood at the head of their ranks. That meant Diomedes and Odysseus must travel to Sykros and return with his son, Neoptolemus. His mood swinging as he seized on this possibility, Menelaus offered his own daughter in marriage to Neoptolemus if that would improve the prospects of the embassy.

Meanwhile, the Trojans were receiving aid of their own in the form of Eurypylus, the son of Telephus, bringing with him a host of Mysians and Ceteians. Noting that Eurypylus' shield depicted all of the labours of Heracles, Paris urged him to strive for martial glory in the coming battle that would rival the mighty deeds of his grandfather. Swearing to never quit the field save in victory or death, Eurypylus led the combined armies into battle.

The faces of the Achaean warlords peer out from the windows of the Trojan Horse – a feature that would have somewhat compromised its intended capacity for subterfuge. Such incongruity notwithstanding, this terracotta amphora uncovered in Mykonos dates from the 7th century BC, making it the oldest physical representation of the horse mythos. (The Art Archive / Alamy)

Bereft of their greatest warriors, the Achaeans were hard pressed. Eurypylus cut down Nireus, then his spear rent Machaon's shoulder and thigh before impaling him through the stomach. Podalirius was ministering to the wounded behind the lines when he learned of his brother's fate. Joining the fray, he slew Lassus and Cleitus with his snake-headed javelin. After a desperate struggle, the Achaeans succeeded in recovering the bodies of Machaon and Nireus, but then their lines broke and most fled for the ships.

The few who rallied around Agamemnon would have been overwhelmed had Aias not cut down Polydamas, and Menelaus wounded Deiphobus, forcing the Trojans to give ground.

When Eurypylus marked this lull in the fighting he turned from the host he had pursued to the ships and fell on the Achaeans still in the field from the rear. Aeneas hurled a great stone that caught Aias in the head and laid him in the dust. His retainers hauled him, scarce drawing breath, from the fray. Fighting back to back, Agamemnon and Menelaus were cut off and surrounded on all sides. The war would have ended right there had the Achaean army not rallied and, led by Teucer and Idomeneus, fought their way through to the aid of their high king.

The toll was high. Eurypylus cut down men of renown and countless numbers of the rank and file. Aeneas slew the Cretan duo Antimachus and Pheres and Paris' arrows laid low Phorcys and Mosynus. Then he shot down Eetion with an arrow through his jaw. Darkness finally ended the day's fighting.

Battle was re-joined in the morning. Again Eurypylus cut down the best the Achaeans could send against him, and he pushed them back to their stockade. From behind the wall they made a stand. The struggle went on through the night and into the next morning. To buy time, the Achaeans had to beg Eurypylus for a two-day truce to deal with their dead. The flames from the pyres rose into the heavens even as Odysseus and Diomedes finally arrived at Skyros.

Deidameia, still mourning for Achilles, was loath to witness her son be consumed by that same war. But Odysseus, sweetening the offer by promising the divine arms and armour of Achilles, convinced Neoptolemus it was his destiny to join the fray. The heroes returned just as Eurypylus stood on the brink of storming the Achaean stockade. Neoptolemus, appearing as Achilles incarnate, rallied the defence and forced the Trojan host to retire.

The following day Neoptolemus, at the head of his father's Myrmidons, and Eurypylus led their armies into battle. Each cut down swathes of the enemy before their inevitable clash. After a long duel, Neoptolemus thrust his spear through the throat of Eurypylus, but the Trojans refused to yield and the fight raged on. Ares and Athena each joined in the slaughter until separated by the anger of Zeus. The mortal antagonists, however, remained locked in combat.

Finally, the Trojans broke and fell back into their city. Carried away in battle frenzy the Achaeans sought to overwhelm the ramparts of Troy, but the defenders rallied on the walls and rained missiles and stones down on their foes The fight only ended when Zeus shrouded the city in an all-encompassing mist.

(OPPOSITE)

Was it fate that that drove Achilles to his doom, leading the assault against the Scaean Gates of Troy? Was it the burnished bronze, gold and silver of his armour, gleaming like a torch in the blood red reflected rays of the sun, making him the most conspicuous target to those defending the walls? Or was it the anger of the archer god Apollo, whose temple the son of Thetis had profaned? Whatever the source of his destruction, it was Paris, leaning far over the battlements, who was its instrument, loosing the fatal arrow that would bring the greatest warrior of a heroic age crashing down to death.

The Fall of Paris

Still the war continued. This time, Calchas prophesied it would not end until Philoctetes, who had been abandoned to his suffering on Lemnos while the black ships were en route to Troy, re-joined the Achaean host. Once again Odysseus and Diomedes were dispatched on an embassy.

When they finally found Philocetes, they were overcome with horror. Philoctetes, so long abandoned, had been reduced to a pitiful state. His wasted body was clothed only in feathers, and still he suffered from the poisonous wound he'd received so many years ago.

Seeing Odysseus and Diomedes approach, Philoctetes reached for his great bow and notched an arrow tipped with the very poison that was tormenting him. But the sweet words of Odysseus dissuaded him from violence and convinced him to join with his former comrades under the walls of Troy.

His wounds dressed by Podalirius, Philoctetes took his place in the line the following morning as the two armies again met on the open plain. Paris loosed a shaft at him, but the Achaean swerved aside and it struck Cleodorus instead, passing clear through his shoulder. Philoctetes' first arrow grazed Paris's wrist, and the Trojan's bow slipped from nerveless fingers. Then the second barbed arrow struck home, burying its deadly venom in Paris's loins.

Paris was borne in agony from the field. Sundown brought an end to the battle, but not to his suffering. Delirious, he sought respite from the healing arts of his forsaken Oenone, but she scorned him, and he died from his wound where his saga began, on the slope of Mt. Ida. Helen wept when the news was brought to her, but more for herself than her deceased husband. With Paris gone there was no place of refuge left for her. Whoever won the war now, she was destined to be some man's possession, not his partner.

In the event, she was claimed by Deiphobus, but the marriage was as unhappy as it was destined to be brief, and hastened the doom of Troy. For Helenus had also desired Helen. Having lost her to his brother, he quit the city only to be captured en route by Odysseus. The Achaeans learned from this disaffected Trojan prince that his city would never fall while the Palladium, an image fashioned in her own likeness by Athena in remorse for the death of Pallas, remained within its walls. Odysseus and Diomedes volunteered to retrieve it and, slipping into the city at night, were able to do so. It was Diomedes who seized the image and, racing ahead, bore it in his arms on their return to the ships. Odysseus, jealous of the fame he would receive, drew his sword to stab Diomedes in the back, but was thwarted by the gleam of moonlight on the blade. Diomedes disarmed and bound the hands of his erstwhile partner and, with the flat of his sword, drove Odysseus before him to the Achaean lines.

The horse being pulled into Troy by Rocío Espín Piñar.

The Wooden Horse

Calchas assembled the chief Achaeans, urging them to accept that Troy was not destined to be overcome by brute force; only by guile and subterfuge might they prevail. It was then that Odysseus presented a new plan. They should offer up a gift to their enemies, a great wooden horse, large enough to conceal a select band of warriors. The rest of the army should burn their tents and sail for Tenedos. When the Trojans saw that the ships were gone, they would draw the horse into the city, and those concealed within would strike.

Of the assembled warlords, only those freshly come to Troy, Neoptolemus and Philoctetes, were keen to continue the battle. The grizzled, burned out veterans, however, immediately seized on Odysseus' plan, and with their approval, the king of Ithaca got down to specifics. Construction of the horse he delegated to Epeius, the master in crafting wood. Athena had brought him a vision of the horse in a dream. The entire army was put at his disposal, and each man toiled at his task obeying Epeius's command. The project was completed in just three days.

Despite his initial hostility to the enterprise, Neoptolemus was the first to enter the horse. After him came Menelaus, then Odysseus, Sthenelus, Diomedes, Philoctetes, Idomeneus, Teucer, and all the boldest and best of the Argives. As its architect, Epeius was the last to take his place, drawing up the ladders and fastening the bolt. With the horse secure, Agamemnon and Nestor oversaw the burning of the tents and then led the ships to Tenedos.

For the gambit to work, someone would have to stay behind, to lull the suspicions of the Trojans. When all others hesitated, a man named Sinon volunteered. Some muttered that he had been less than conspicuously valiant over the course of the conflict, but whatever qualities he lacked on the battlefield, he displayed extraordinary courage in this new role

So the Achaeans sailed away, leaving only the wooden horse and Sinon behind. When the Trojans ventured out from behind their great walls, they found Sinon, huddled amidst the remains of the enemy camp. Wary and vindictive, the Trojans tortured poor Sinon, sheering away his ears and nose, in an agony of interrogation. But he never deviated from the cover story Odysseus had concocted for him. The Achaeans, weary of ceaseless war, had sailed for home. The horse was an offering to Athena to offset her wrath for the palladium stolen from Troy. Sinon was to have been sacrificed to Poseidon as surety for a safe voyage, but had thrown himself at the feet of the horse for sanctuary. Fearing to anger Athena, his former comrades had abandoned him there.

As the Trojans debated what to do, Laocoon, Poseidon's priest, urged his compatriots to burn the horse lest it be a trap. To prove his point, he threw a spear against the flanks of the horse. The point punched clean through, leaving the shaft vibrating in the hollow belly, its rattle echoing for all to hear. To shut him up, Athena afflicted Laocoon with intolerable pain, but the priest would not be silent, even when the goddess struck him blind. She finally resorted to summoning two serpents from their lair on the isle of Calydna. The Trojans fled in panic as the serpents snatched up the two sons of Laocoon in their jaws and dragged them, still reaching for their sightless father with pleading hands, beneath the Earth. Seeing in this the penalty for defiance of the gods, the Trojans lashed long ropes to the horse and dragged it into their city, into the temple of Athena. Leaving it there festooned with flowers, the Trojans gathered around, and marvelled as they gazed at the mighty work.

Signs and portents of impending disaster were everywhere. When offerings were made to the gods, the flames died out, as if under heavy, hissing rain, and the wreaths of smoke writhed blood-red. But amidst the delirious joy of a city liberated from a decade of war, only one heart was steadfast, one soul clear-eyed. Cassandra, the prophetic daughter of Priam, shrieked out a warning of imminent catastrophe. She grabbed a brand of blazing pine-wood from the fire and ran towards the horse. Priam's guards intercepted her, and, on his orders, she was dragged away, still begging the city to come to its senses.

There was one last challenge to the Achaean subterfuge, when Helen herself came out and strolled around the horse three times. She trailed her fingers against its smooth flanks, calling out each Achaean warlord by name,

Giovanni Domenico Tiepolo's *Procession of the Trojan Horse into Troy*. Ensnared by the stratagem of Odysseus, the guile of Sinon, and the craft of Epeius, the Trojans laboured to consummate their own doom. (The Art Archive / Alamy)

and mimicking the voices of their wives. Diomedes and Menelaus wavered between springing out then and there or trying to answer Helen from the inside. It was Odysseus who kept them in check, all except Anticlus, who could not restrain himself from calling out in response. Odysseus had no choice but to clap both hands over his mouth, and kept them there, choking the life out of this wayward comrade in arms to save the lives of all the rest.

So the celebrations continued long into the night. Finally, the festivities sputtered out and with the revelers, the lights. Troy lay covered in drunken oblivion even as the Achaean fleet crept closer, sailing from Tenedos with a fair wind at its back, a gift from Thetis. Hearing only silence, the heroes at last emerged from inside the horse. The first to do so, Echion, son of Portheus, was killed in his eagerness when he misjudged the distance to the ground and leapt to his death. Quickly, silently, the others eliminated the few guards that still held their posts and opened the city gates. It was midnight, and the clear moon was rising. Sinon, having been left unguarded, signalled to the fleet with a torch that the gates were open. The Achaean ships disgorged their warriors who, frenzied with the opportunity stormed into the city.

Flame and Fortune

A hideous massacre ensued. The Trojans, asleep and heavy with wine were easy prey. The lucky ones were killed outright; others, mutilated in their sleep, crawled blind and bloody amongst the dying and the dead. The women were cut down next to their men, or worse. Many begged their husbands to kill them before they were taken by the enemy.

Though they knew that the city was lost, the defenders fought back with whatever they had at hand, and many an Argive was cut down in his hour of victory with burning brands snatched from the hearth or spits torn from the roast.

Of all Troy's allies only one was alerted to the danger. Virgil describes how the shade of Hector came to Aeneas in a dream, urging him to flee.

Aeneas rallied what men he could find, including Coroebus, the son of King Mygdon of Phrygia, who suggested donning Achaean shields and gear. Thus disguised, they fought their way to where the fiercest fighting raged at the heart of the city, around Priam's palace. There the Trojans cannibalized their own halls and towers for the weapons of last resort, hurling rubble, beams and rafters down upon their foes.

But nothing could hold back the tide of the Achaean assault. At its front, charged Neoptolemus, whose rage proved the equal of his father. He slew enemies by the dozen, granting mercy to none. Finally, he reached the royal chambers and found Priam himself. The old king, a broken man, accepted his doom without fear or resistance. Neoptolemus struck his head off with one clean stroke.

Deeper into the heart of Troy drove the Achaeans. Menelaus found Deiphobus in his chambers and systematically hacked him to pieces. Helen fled into the palace, but Menelaus tracked her down, hungering to slay her in his jealous rage, until Aphrodite intervened. Cassandra, meanwhile, sought refuge in the temple of Athena, only to be dragged from the altar of the goddess and raped by the lust-maddened Aias. This sacrilege was too much even for the Achaeans, whose hostility forced him, ironically, to seek shelter at the very altar he had just desecrated.

As the night waned, Troy entered her death throes. Flames roared around Apollo's temple and on all sides the buildings crumbled to ruin. The battle was lost, and the few surviving Trojans fled. Amongst them was Aeneas, who left the city, a sea of fire, bearing his father Anchises on his shoulders and leading his son Ascanius by the hand. Amidst the chaos, Aeneas lost his wife, Priam's daughter Creusa. All he had left as he fled into exile was a random handful of dazed survivors.

Aftermath

With any remaining threat neutralized, the Argives were finally free to indulge their long pent-up passion for looting. Amidst the background of pillage and ruin, Menelaus at last led Helen from the smouldering city, her head covered in a dark veil.

The other Trojan women were not so lucky. Each Achaean warlord took a highborn trophy back with him for the journey home. Cassandra was Agamemnon's prize. Neoptolemus took Andromache. Hecuba was parcelled out to Odysseus, as a slave to the treacherous foe she loathed above all others. But her nightmare was just beginning. First, she lost her grandchild, Astyanax. Odysseus tore the boy from Andromache's arms, led the last prince of Troy onto the battlements, and hurled him from the high walls to his death. Andromache, having lost her husband, had now lost her only child, and all her hope.

Then, as Neoptolemus slept, the shade of his father urged him to inform the Achaeans, Agamemnon above all, of his demand that Priam's daughter Polyxeina be sacrificed in his memory. Otherwise, his wrath against them

(OVERLEAF)
Dawn on the morning after the night of the horse offered a final glimpse of their city to the last survivors of Troy. She was still burning, the smoke rising up to the heavens and the pitiless gods. Broken and bereft, the refugees would cling to their sole remaining champion, Aeneas, as they passed into exile. They faced a long journey, but at its end lay a new home and the seeds of future glory.

would burn brighter than for Briseis. None paid heed to Hecuba's lament that it was her blood in exchange for a dead man's rage. For Neoptolemus butchered the Trojan princess on his father's tomb, drenching Polyxeina's virgin flesh in her own gore.

This loss was more than Hecuba could bear. Invoking dire curses against the Achaeans, she continued to provoke them until, to shut her up, they stoned her to death. For the Argives, it was time, at last, to sail for home. Their ships rode low in the water, packed as they were with the spoils of war. But their departure was overshadowed by ill omens. Menelaus was for departing at once, and this displeased Agamemnon, who thought the host should first offer sacrifices to appease the anger of Athena. The two brothers nearly came to blows and parted on bad terms. They would never lay eyes on each other again.

Agamemnon was right to be concerned, for Athena nursed a bitter grudge towards Aias for his violation of Cassandra at the altar within her temple.

The women of a fallen city were the legitimate booty of war in antiquity. But Aias went too far when he dragged Cassandra, clinging to the Xoanon, the wooden cult image of Athena, from the sanctuary of her temple. For this profanity, represented here in a fresco from the atrium of the Casa del Menandro in Pompeii, his own comrades in arms nearly stoned him to death; the goddess would have her revenge shortly thereafter. (PD)

TROY TODAY

Though the history and even location of Troy faded into the shadows at the end of the classical era, the myth lived on through medieval folklore and burst back into the limelight when the original texts were rediscovered during the Renaissance. Giovanni Boccaccio's *Il Filostrato* inspired Geoffrey Chaucer's *Troilus and Criseyde*, which served as the basis for Shakespeare's *Troilus and Cressida*, which in turn was adapted by John Dryden. Subsequent stage adaptations have run the gamut of socio-political commentary, from Heinrich von Kleist's *Penthesilea* (1808) to Jean Giraudoux's *La Guerre de Troie N'aura pas Lieus* (1935). Facets of the saga have played out in operas by Mozart, Lully, Piccinni, Purcell and Berlioz, and saturate modern popular culture, from art and sculpture to TV, videogames and graphic novels (the Marvel Comics version by Roy Thomas and Miguel Angel Sepulveda is a vivid recreation, while the *Age of Bronze* series by Eric Shanower, which strips all of the mythological aspects from the story to relate an entirely secular interpretation, is highly recommended). Since its celluloid debut in *Le Jugement de Paris* (1902), the tragedy of Troy has featured in numerous films worldwide, including *La Caduta di Troia* (1911), *Helena* (1924), *Helen of Troy* (1956), *L'ira di Achille* (1962), and *La Guerra di Troia* (1962). The most recent version, *Troy* (2004), a big-budget Hollywood production, played the saga "straight" as a pseudo-historical narrative bereft of divine intervention. The movie boasted a suitably heroic scale, a vivid palate, and impressive combat sequences, particularly the climactic duel before the Scaean Gate. Perhaps its boldest ploy was to feature a Helen who was only the fourth most beautiful character on display, behind the male leads Brad Pitt (Achilles), Eric Bana (Hector) and Orlando Bloom (Paris). Finally, bringing us back to where we started, those wanting to appreciate the original canon in a fresh new voice might like to read the *Iliad* in the translation of Christopher Logue.

Enlisting the support of Zeus and Poseidon, she unleashed a monstrous storm. Aias' ship was blasted to pieces. Into the depths sank both Achaeans and their captives, some of whom flung their arms round the horrified heads of their erstwhile captors, dragging them down to mutual death.

The fleet of Menelaus was also shattered by the storm. Only after eight years of misadventure were he and Helen able to return to Sparta. They, at least, were welcomed home. Teucer and Idomeneus were hounded into exile. Agamemnon did not have long to enjoy his triumph. In his absence, Clytemnestra had taken a lover, her husband's cousin, Aegisthus. They snared the high king in nets in his own bed, then slaughtered him and Cassandra.

Neoptolemus, heeding the advice of his grandmother Thetis, burned his ships and took the land route home, bearing his prize, Andromache, with him. Later, he married Hermione, the daughter of Menelaus and Helen. Outraged, Orestes, who had been previously promised the hand of Hermione, slew Achilles' son.

Of all those who fought at Troy the longest sojourns in the aftermath were those of Odysseus and Aeneas, but their tales belong to other texts.

When the Achaeans had at last all departed, Poseidon, scorning the aspirations of men to immortal deeds, turned his wrath on the stockade they had built to shelter their ships during the long years of the siege. When his waves abated, no sign was left of the war or the mighty endeavours that had

The Death of Priam a 1785 oil painting by Jean-Baptiste Regnault. Neoptolemus took the old king's head off with one stroke; Quintus Smyrnaeus describes how the body fell "amidst dark-purple blood and slaughtered men. So lay he, chiefest once of all the world in lineage, wealth, in many and goodly sons." (Musee de Picardie, Amiens, France / Giraudon / The Bridgeman Art Library)

transpired therein, save tombs, a ruined city, and standing in its midst, a great, hollow, empty, horse.

But this was the beginning, not the end, of the legend. Those who fought for Troy, and those who fought against her, live still. Their battles rage every day, their stories are told and retold.

In the words of Agathias:

> "O City, where are the once proud walls,
> the temples heavy with riches?
> Gone,
> lost to War,
> and Time,
> and to bleak Fate,
> and to harsh Envy.
> But the name of Troy,
> and the glory of Troy,
> shall live to see these die.

BIBLIOGRAPHY

Reading the *Iliad* is of course the essential introduction to the Trojan War. Beyond Homer, however, the trail becomes more elusive. The fact that the saga has come to us fragmented, from the pens of a host of different authors, is both a blessing and a curse. A blessing, in that it has enabled the legendary Helen of Troy to survive the intervening age between oral folklore and digital mass-media; a curse, in that it has allowed a host of rival interpretations to compromise our ever arriving at the original, "true" narrative of the story. Did Iphigenia, for example, willingly sacrifice herself at Aulis, as Euripides portrayed it? Or was she caught unawares and dragged to the altar like an animal, gagged so that her final words might not be a curse called down upon her house, according to the version of Aeschylus? After the death in battle of Penthesilia, did the Achaeans offer her remains the honours of war, as Quintus Smyrnaeus relates? Or, having captured her, mortally wounded, did they debate whether "to throw her, while still alive enough to have feeling, either into the river to drown or out for the dogs to tear apart," as was recorded by Dictys of Crete? Piecing together a coherent, singular account means making subjective decisions as to who's version of events should be included. In the interests of equal time, the discerning reader is invited to explore the sources listed below to construct an interpretation of his or her own.

All quotes from the *Iliad* included in this work were drawn from the translation by Robert Fagles listed below.

Primary Sources

Aeschylus, *The Oresteia*, translated by Ted Hughes, Farrar, Straus, and Giroux, New York, 1999.

Apollodorus, *Epitome*, translated by J.G. Frazer, available online at: http://www.theoi.com/Text/ApollodorusE.html.

Dictys of Crete, *Journal of the Trojan War*, translated by R. M. Frazer, Jr., Indiana University Press, Bloomington, 1966.

Euripides, *Iphigenia in Aulis and The Trojan Women*, translated by J. Michael Walton, Methuen Drama, London, 1991.

Homer, *The Iliad*, translated by Robert Fagles, Viking, New York, 1990.

Homer, *The Odyssey*, translated by Robert Fagles, Viking, New York, 1996.

Hyginus, Gaius Julius, *Fabulae*, translated by Mary Grant, available online at: http://www.theoi.com/Text/HyginusFabulae1.html.

Smyrnaeus, Quintus, *The Fall of Troy*, translated by Arthur S. May, Harvard University Press, Cambridge, 1962.

Sophocles, *Philoctetes*, translated by Hanna Roisman, Duckworth, London, 2005.

Stesichorus, *The Sack of Troy and The Wooden Horse*, Proceedings of the Cambridge Philological Society, Vol. 19, January 1973, pp. 47-65.

Statius, Publius Papinius, *Achilleid*, translated by A.O.W. Dilke, Harvard University Press, Cambridge, 1954.

Tryphiodorus, *The Taking of Ilios*, translated by A.W. Mair, available online at: http://www.theoi.com/Text/Tryphiodorus.html.

Virgil, *The Aeneid*, translated by Robert Fagles, Viking, New York, 2006.

West. M.L., *Greek Epic Fragments from the Seventh to the Fifth Centuries* BC, Harvard University Press, Cambridge, 2003 (incorporating *Lesches of Pyrrha, The Little Iliad*; *Arktinos of Miletos, The Aethiopis and The Sack of Ilium*; the various authors of *The Cypria*; and the fragments of the *Nostoi*).

Secondary Sources

Alexander, Caroline; *The War that Killed Achilles: The True Story of Homer's Iliad and the Trojan War*, Viking, New York, 2009.

Andersen, Øivind, & Dickie, Matthew (eds.); *Homer's World: Fiction, Tradition, Reality*, P. Åström, Bergen, 1995.

Bryce, Trevor R.; "The Trojan War: Is there Truth behind the Legend?" Near Eastern Archaeology, Vol. 65, No. 3, September 2002, pp. 182-195.

Burgess, Jonathan S.; *The Tradition of the Trojan War in Homer and the Epic Cycle*, Johns Hopkins University Press, Baltimore, 2001.

Korfmann, Manfred; "Was There a Trojan War?" Archaeology, Vol. 57, No. 3, May-June 2004, pp. 36-41.

Redfield, James M.; *Nature and Culture in the Iliad: The Tragedy of Hector*, Duke University Press, Durham, 1994.

Shay, Jonathan; *Achilles in Vietnam: Combat Trauma and the Undoing of Character*, Simon & Schuster, New York, 1995.

Strauss, Barry S.; *The Trojan War: A New History*, Simon & Schuster, New York, 2006.

Weil, Simone; McCarthy, Mary; Bespaloff, Rachel; *War and the Iliad*, New York Review of Books, New York, 2005.

Wood, Michael; *In Search of the Trojan War*, Facts on File, New York, 1985.